Mathematics for Christian Living Series

Mathematics for Christian Living Series

Working Arithmetic

Grade 2

Workbook 4, Lessons 124–170

Rod and Staff Publishers, Inc.
PO Box 3
Crockett, Kentucky 41413
Telephone: (606) 522-4348

Acknowledgments

We are indebted to God for the vision and enabling grace to develop the *Mathematics for Christian Living Series*. We thank Him for supplying the needed funds to cover the costs of research and development.

This revision was written by Sister Joanna Nighswander. Brother Merlin Heatwole and Brother Marvin Eicher edited the course. The work was evaluated by a panel of reviewers and tested by teachers in several classrooms. The artwork was done by Sister Marian Baltozer and Sister Bethany Showalter. Much effort was devoted to the production of the book. We are grateful for all who have helped to make this book possible.

—*The Publishers*

This workbook is part of a course for grade 2 arithmetic and will be most effective if used with the other parts of the course. *Working Arithmetic* includes the following items:

Books and Worksheets

2 Teacher's Manuals
4 Pupil's Workbooks
2 Practice Sheets Workbooks
Reproducible Supplemental Pack, which contains:

- My 1,000 Book
- Individual Student Flash Cards for Triplet Facts
- Number Line Patterns
- Boat Poster Pattern
- Clover Patch Poster Pattern
- Blossom Charts Pattern
- Place Value Chart Pattern
- Thermometer Pattern

Rod and Staff Publishers, Inc.
Crockett, Kentucky 41413

Printed in USA

ISBN 978-07399-0723-8

Catalog no. 132244

2 3 4 5 6 — 30 29 28 27 26 25 24 23 22 21

Workbook 4 Contents

This list shows what concepts are introduced in these lessons. Each concept is also reviewed in following lessons.

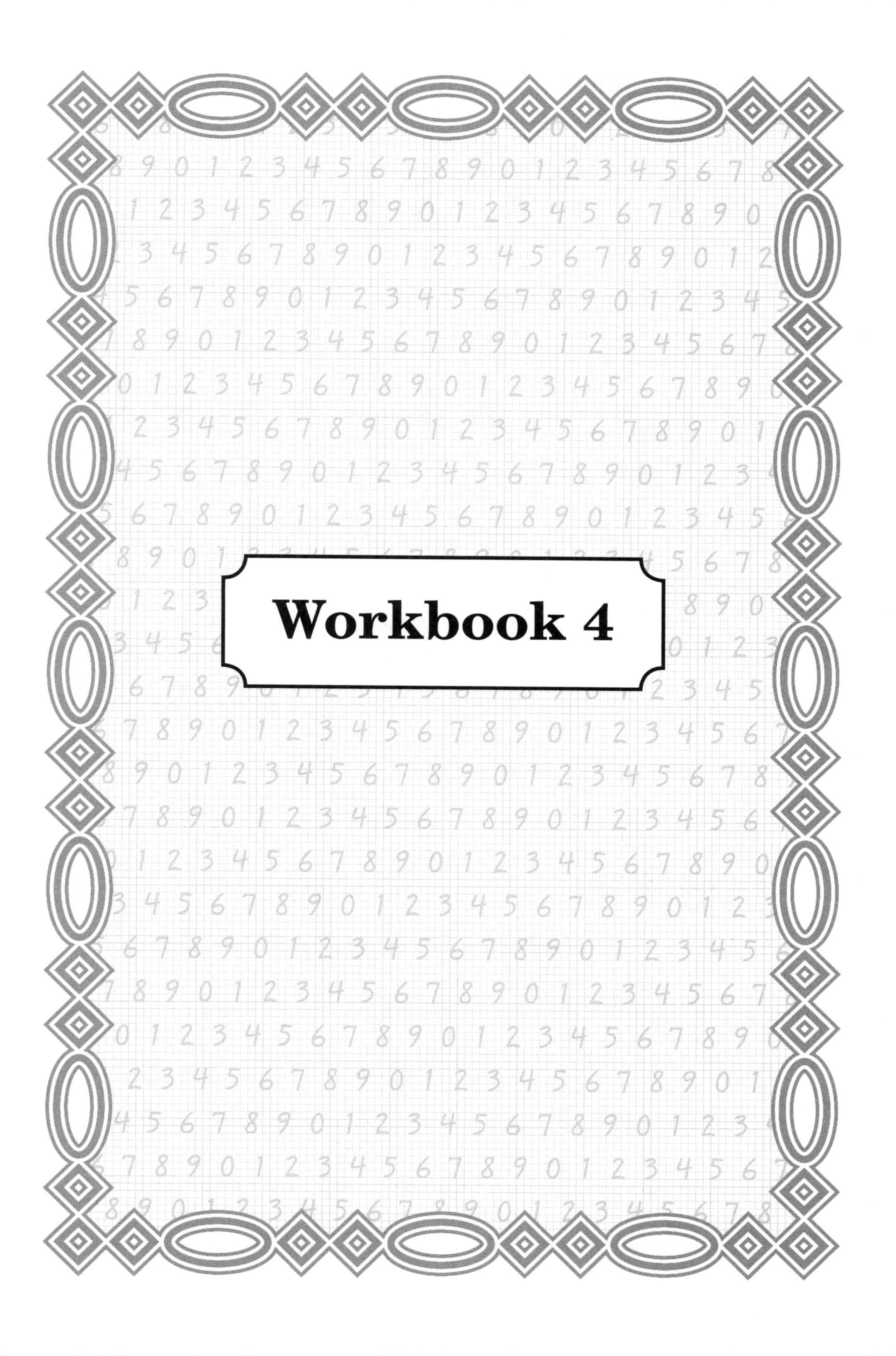
Workbook 4

Fill in the whole and the parts.

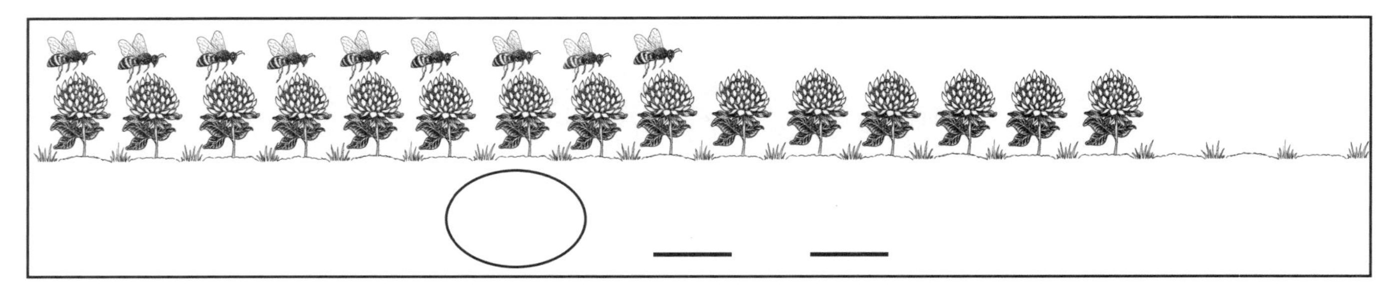

Write a fact for each picture.

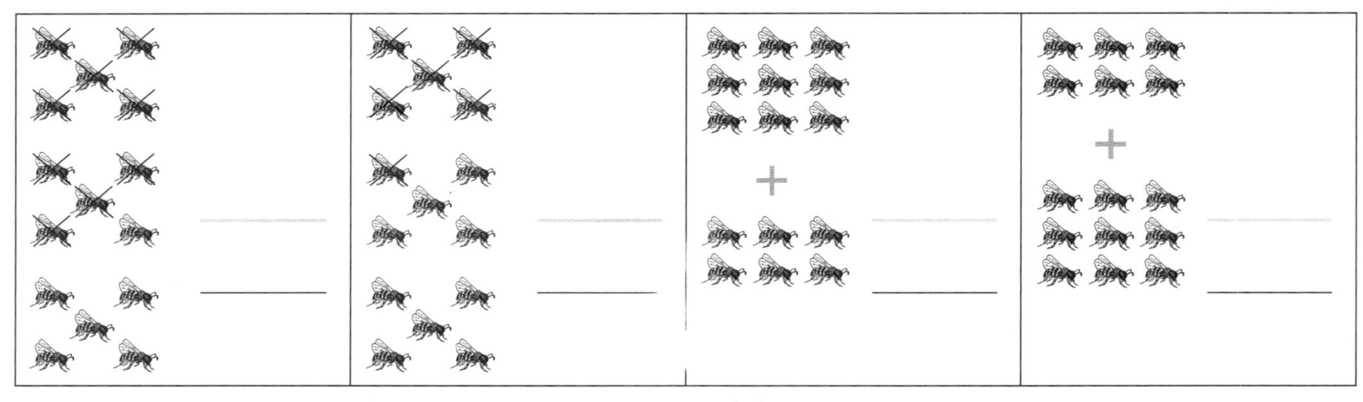

Trace and copy the triplet. Write the facts twice in the hives.

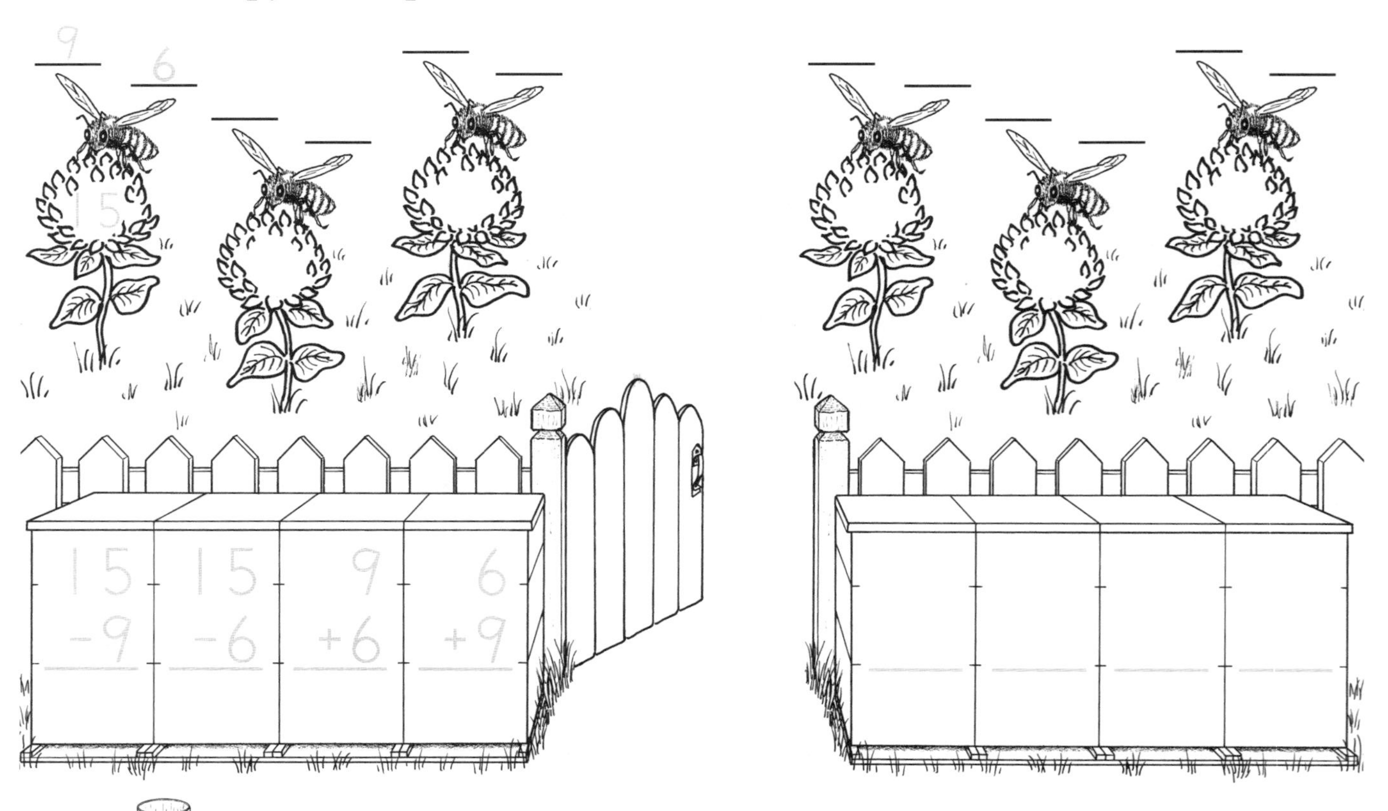

"The Lord shall bring thee into the land . . . flowing with milk and honey."

Exodus 13:5

Answer these facts.

15	6	7	5	15	15	13	9
− 6	+ 9	+ 7	+ 8	− 9	− 6	− 5	+ 6

14	6	15	9	13	6	8	15
− 7	+ 9	− 6	+ 6	− 5	+ 9	+ 5	− 9

6	14	15	7	9	13	15	15
+ 9	− 7	− 9	+ 7	+ 6	− 8	− 6	− 9

If it's 1 child on a swing
Or 15 bees on wing,
*"His eye seeth
every precious thing."*
If it's 300 busy ants,
Or 400 tiny plants,
*"His eye seeth
every precious thing."*

8	15	15	9
+ 5	− 6	− 9	+ 6

Answer these problems. Carry when you need to.

86	159	71	83	128	155
+ 59	− 66	+ 63	+ 67	− 66	− 61

147	69	60	76	139	156
− 54	+ 76	+ 90	+ 58	− 45	− 94

124 **Answer these story problems.**

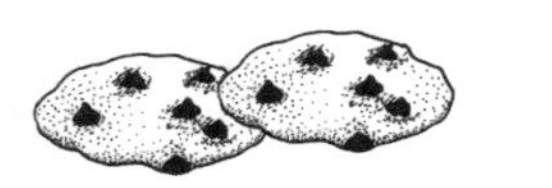

Mother made 98 cookies. She gave 65 to a family in need. How many cookies did she have left?

Freda's family lived 14 miles from the church. Mae's family lived 5 miles from the church. When they traveled to church, how many more miles did Freda's family travel than Mae's family?

Count the money. Write the amount two ways.

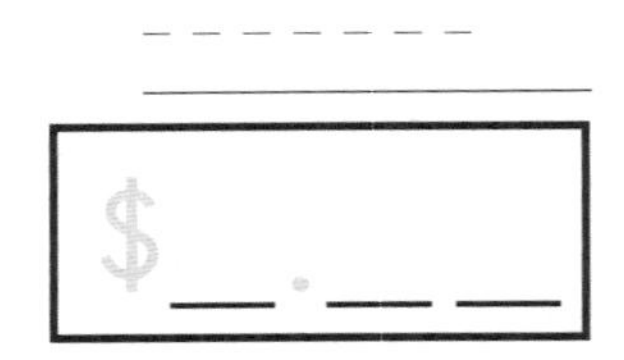

$ ___ . ___ ___

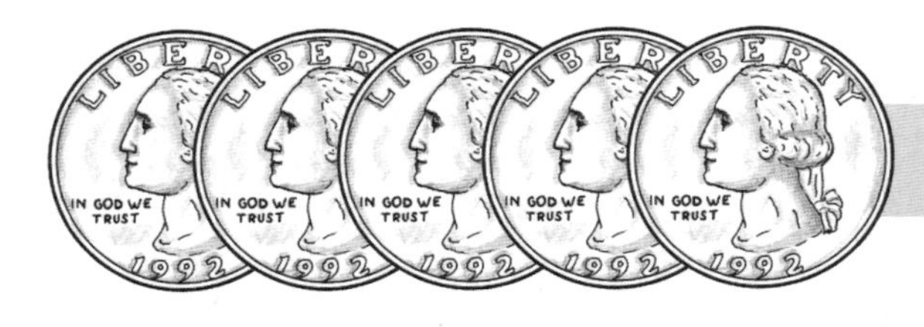

$ ___ . ___ ___

Trace and finish the rule.

2 cups = ____ ________

Speed Drill

"Let us run with patience the race that is set before us."
Hebrews 12:1

14	13	12	14	13	14
- 5	- 9	- 6	- 7	- 4	- 8

13	14	14	12	13	14
- 8	- 6	- 5	- 4	- 7	- 9

12	14	13	12	14	13	12	14
- 7	- 8	- 6	- 5	- 9	- 5	- 3	- 7

5	3	3	2	2	5	4	3
2	4	2	7	6	4	2	5
+ 7	+ 5	+ 8	+ 5	+ 6	+ 4	+ 6	+ 6

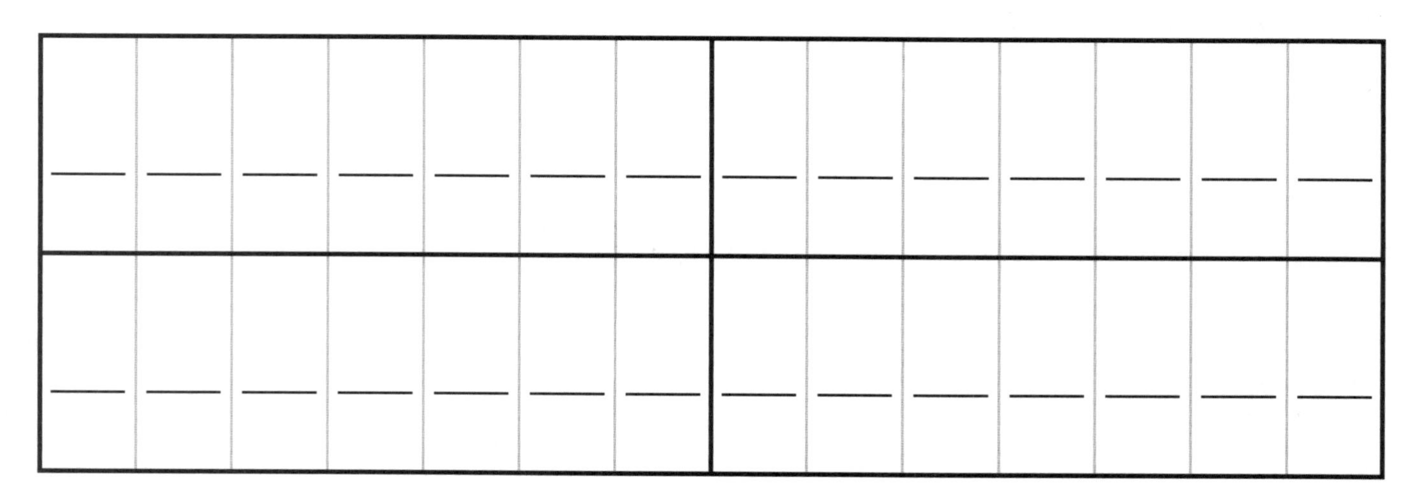

125 Fill in the whole and the parts.

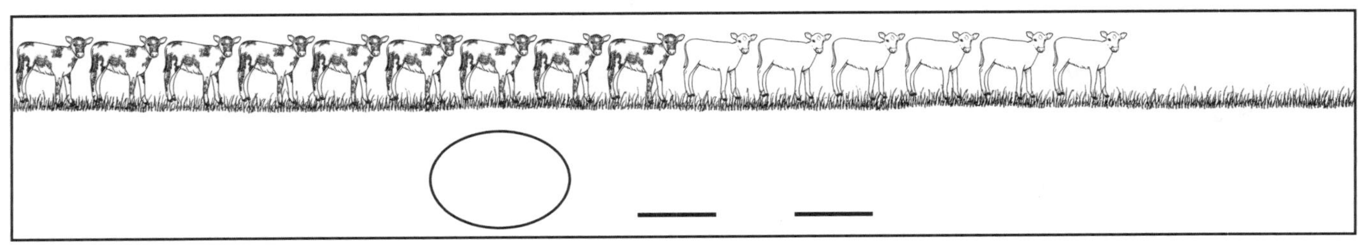

Answer the facts. Make the pictures fit the facts.
Your barn can look like this one.

Trace and copy the triplet.

Write the four facts twice.

"And I will send grass
in thy fields for thy cattle,
that thou mayest eat and be full."
Deuteronomy 11:15

Answer these facts.

125

$$\begin{array}{r} 6 \\ +\ 9 \\ \hline \end{array} \quad \begin{array}{r} 14 \\ -\ 6 \\ \hline \end{array} \quad \begin{array}{r} 15 \\ -\ 9 \\ \hline \end{array} \quad \begin{array}{r} 5 \\ +\ 9 \\ \hline \end{array} \quad \begin{array}{r} 9 \\ +\ 6 \\ \hline \end{array} \quad \begin{array}{r} 6 \\ +\ 8 \\ \hline \end{array} \quad \begin{array}{r} 15 \\ -\ 6 \\ \hline \end{array} \quad \begin{array}{r} 6 \\ +\ 9 \\ \hline \end{array}$$

$$\begin{array}{r} 15 \\ -\ 6 \\ \hline \end{array} \quad \begin{array}{r} 6 \\ +\ 9 \\ \hline \end{array} \quad \begin{array}{r} 9 \\ +\ 5 \\ \hline \end{array} \quad \begin{array}{r} 9 \\ +\ 6 \\ \hline \end{array} \quad \begin{array}{r} 5 \\ +\ 9 \\ \hline \end{array} \quad \begin{array}{r} 15 \\ -\ 6 \\ \hline \end{array} \quad \begin{array}{r} 8 \\ +\ 6 \\ \hline \end{array} \quad \begin{array}{r} 15 \\ -\ 9 \\ \hline \end{array}$$

$$\begin{array}{r} 6 \\ +\ 9 \\ \hline \end{array} \quad \begin{array}{r} 14 \\ -\ 5 \\ \hline \end{array} \quad \begin{array}{r} 6 \\ +\ 8 \\ \hline \end{array} \quad \begin{array}{r} 15 \\ -\ 9 \\ \hline \end{array} \quad \begin{array}{r} 15 \\ -\ 6 \\ \hline \end{array} \quad \begin{array}{r} 6 \\ +\ 9 \\ \hline \end{array} \quad \begin{array}{r} 14 \\ -\ 9 \\ \hline \end{array} \quad \begin{array}{r} 9 \\ +\ 6 \\ \hline \end{array}$$

$$\begin{array}{r} 9 \\ +\ 5 \\ \hline \end{array} \quad \begin{array}{r} 15 \\ -\ 6 \\ \hline \end{array} \quad \begin{array}{r} 15 \\ -\ 9 \\ \hline \end{array} \quad \begin{array}{r} 6 \\ +\ 9 \\ \hline \end{array} \quad \begin{array}{r} 14 \\ -\ 8 \\ \hline \end{array} \quad \begin{array}{r} 9 \\ +\ 6 \\ \hline \end{array}$$

Answer these problems. Carry or borrow when you need to.

$$\begin{array}{r} 85 \\ -\ 61 \\ \hline \end{array} \quad \begin{array}{r} 69 \\ +\ 36 \\ \hline \end{array} \quad \begin{array}{r} 95 \\ -\ 76 \\ \hline \end{array} \quad \begin{array}{r} 76 \\ +\ 39 \\ \hline \end{array} \quad \begin{array}{r} 85 \\ +\ 49 \\ \hline \end{array} \quad \begin{array}{r} 95 \\ -\ 39 \\ \hline \end{array}$$

$$\begin{array}{r} 73 \\ -\ 17 \\ \hline \end{array} \quad \begin{array}{r} 99 \\ -\ 75 \\ \hline \end{array} \quad \begin{array}{r} 81 \\ +\ 24 \\ \hline \end{array} \quad \begin{array}{r} 64 \\ -\ 45 \\ \hline \end{array} \quad \begin{array}{r} 59 \\ +\ 56 \\ \hline \end{array} \quad \begin{array}{r} 72 \\ +\ 62 \\ \hline \end{array}$$

125 Measure these lines.

Write the time.

Answer these story problems.

Three families at Grassy Ridge have farms. The Millers have 23 cows, the Hooks have 45, and the Steiners have 2. How many cows do the Grassy Ridge farmers have?

Mother had one dozen oranges in a bag. She gave 6 of them to Mrs. Gray. How many oranges are in Mother's bag now?

Trace and finish the rule.

______ ______________ = 1 pint

Count by 5's.

100

126 Fill in the whole and the parts. Write the facts.

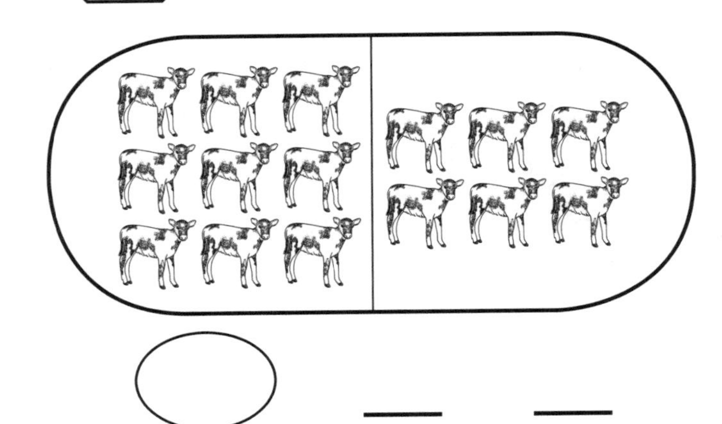

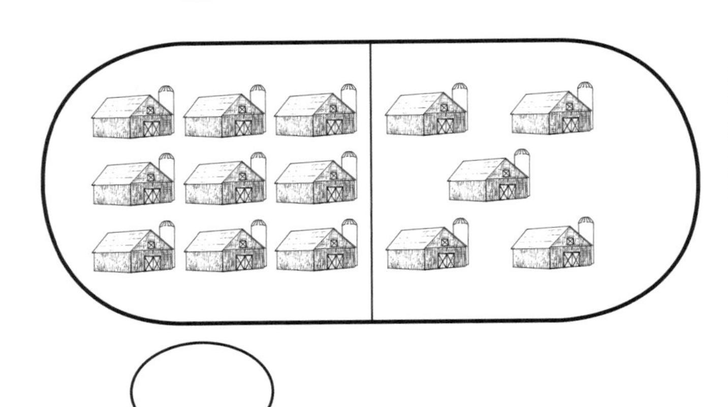

Fill in the missing whole or part.

$15 - \_\_\_ = 9$

$\_\_\_ - 8 = 6$

$9 + 6 = \_\_\_$

$\_\_\_ - 6 = 9$

$\_\_\_ + 9 = 15$

$8 + 6 = \_\_\_$

$\_\_\_ + 6 = 15$

$9 + \_\_\_ = 15$

$15 - \_\_\_ = 6$

$6 + 9 = \_\_\_$

$\_\_\_ - 6 = 8$

$15 - 6 = \_\_\_$

$\_\_\_ + 6 = 14$

$9 + \_\_\_ = 15$

$6 + 8 = \_\_\_$

$\_\_\_ - 9 = 6$

$15 - \_\_\_ = 9$

$6 + \_\_\_ = 15$

Answer these problems. Borrow when you need to.

95	84	74	95	94	93
- 9	- 8	- 2	- 6	- 7	- 5
___	___	___	___	___	___

89	94	94	99	75	83
-37	-88	-89	-78	-46	-74
___	___	___	___	___	___

62	53	85	99	64	45
-24	-37	-29	-67	-38	-36
___	___	___	___	___	___

Measure these lines.

Trace and finish the rule.

7 days = ____ ________

2 cups = ____ ________

126 Answer these story problems.

David was king in Jerusalem for 33 years. Before that, he had been king in Hebron for 7 years. How many years was David king?

Jacob served Laban 7 years for Leah and 7 years for Rachel. How many years did Jacob work to get his wives?

Besides the years he worked for his wives, Jacob worked 6 more years for animals. What was the total number of years that Jacob served Laban? Use your answer from the last problem to help answer this one.

Write a fraction for the shaded part of each picture.

Speed Drill

"Let us run
with patience the race
that is set before us."
Hebrews 12:1

6	15	15	14	9	6
+ 9	− 9	− 6	− 8	+ 6	+ 8

6	6	15	8	9	15
+ 8	+ 9	− 9	+ 6	+ 6	− 6

9	14	6	15	8	15	9	14
+ 6	− 8	+ 9	− 6	+ 6	− 9	+ 6	− 6

15	6	14	15	6	15	9	14
− 6	+ 8	− 6	− 9	+ 9	− 6	+ 6	− 8

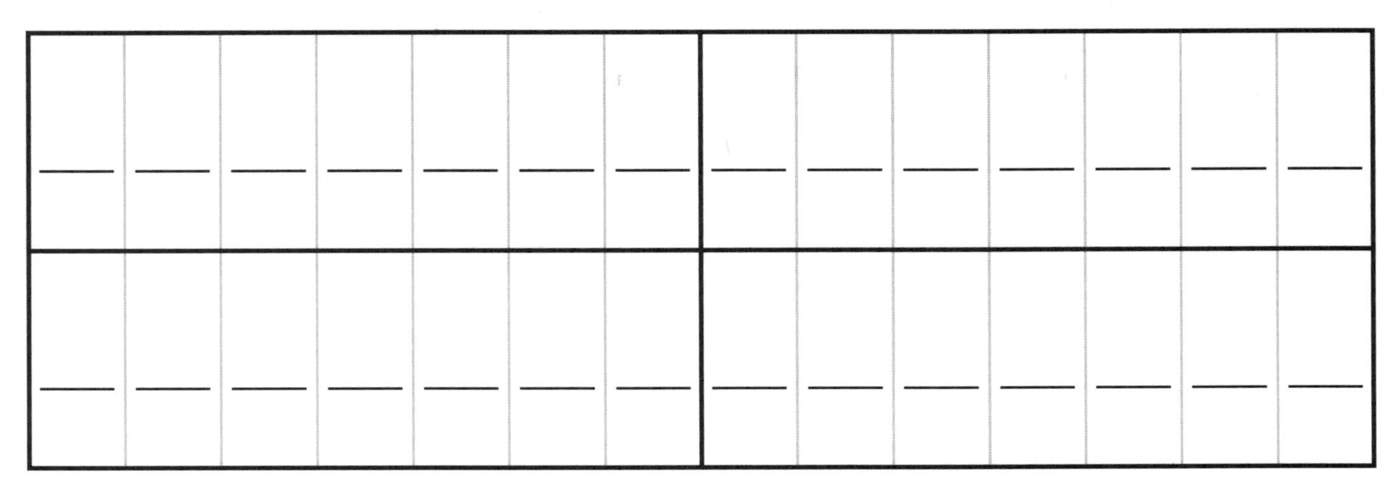

127

Fill in the whole and the parts. Write the facts.

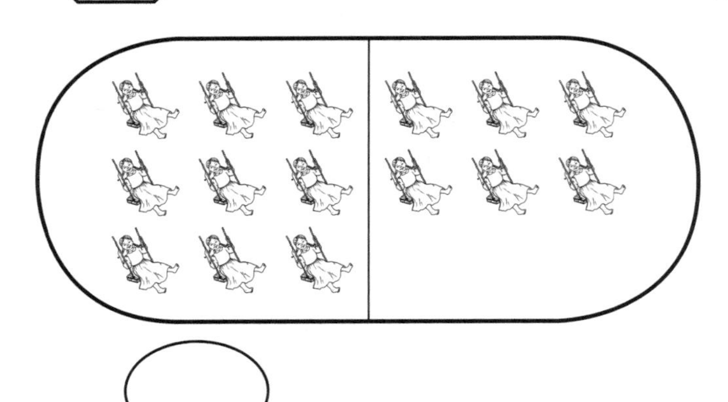

Answer these facts.

$13 - 8$	$9 + 6$	$8 + 4$	$15 - 6$	$9 + 4$	$14 - 5$	$6 + 8$	$12 - 3$
$14 - 7$	$6 + 7$	$8 + 6$	$12 - 8$	$9 + 6$	$8 + 5$	$15 - 9$	$4 + 9$
$9 + 3$	$9 + 5$	$15 - 9$	$5 + 8$	$14 - 8$	$7 + 6$	$6 + 9$	$13 - 4$
$9 + 6$	$13 - 6$	$14 - 6$	$6 + 9$	$3 + 9$	$7 + 7$	$15 - 6$	$13 - 5$

Answer these story problems.

Grandmother gave books to the children. Lee's book has 93 pages. Fay's book has 63 pages. What is the difference in the number of pages?

Mother bought stickers. She paid 90¢ for one pack and 60¢ for another pack. How much did she pay for both packs of stickers?

$ __.____

Answer these problems. You will need to carry one or two times in each problem.

$$\begin{array}{r}258\\+382\\\hline\end{array}\quad\begin{array}{r}273\\+574\\\hline\end{array}\quad\begin{array}{r}588\\+265\\\hline\end{array}\quad\begin{array}{r}445\\+489\\\hline\end{array}\quad\begin{array}{r}216\\+659\\\hline\end{array}$$

$$\begin{array}{r}436\\+269\\\hline\end{array}\quad\begin{array}{r}426\\+134\\\hline\end{array}\quad\begin{array}{r}286\\+248\\\hline\end{array}\quad\begin{array}{r}309\\+396\\\hline\end{array}\quad\begin{array}{r}114\\+446\\\hline\end{array}$$

$$\begin{array}{r}583\\+257\\\hline\end{array}\quad\begin{array}{r}349\\+526\\\hline\end{array}\quad\begin{array}{r}456\\+478\\\hline\end{array}\quad\begin{array}{r}459\\+394\\\hline\end{array}\quad\begin{array}{r}172\\+675\\\hline\end{array}$$

127

Use the calendar page to answer the questions.

July						
Sunday	Monday	Tuesday	Wednesday	Thursday	Friday	Saturday
		1	2	3	4	5
6	7	8	9	10	11	12
13	14	15	16	17	18	19
20	21	22	23	24	25	26
27	28	29	30	31		

1. The month of ____________________ has __________ days.
2. The Martin family had visitors on the 13th, which is a

   ____________________.
3. John's birthday is on the last Tuesday of this month. What is the date of John's birthday? ____________________ __________
4. Aunt Miriam is planning to come on the 28th. That will be on a

   ____________________.

Trace and finish the rule.

______ ____________ = 1 week

Name the days of the week.

____________________, ____________________, ____________________,

____________________, ____________________,

____________________, ____________________

Count the money. Add the amounts.

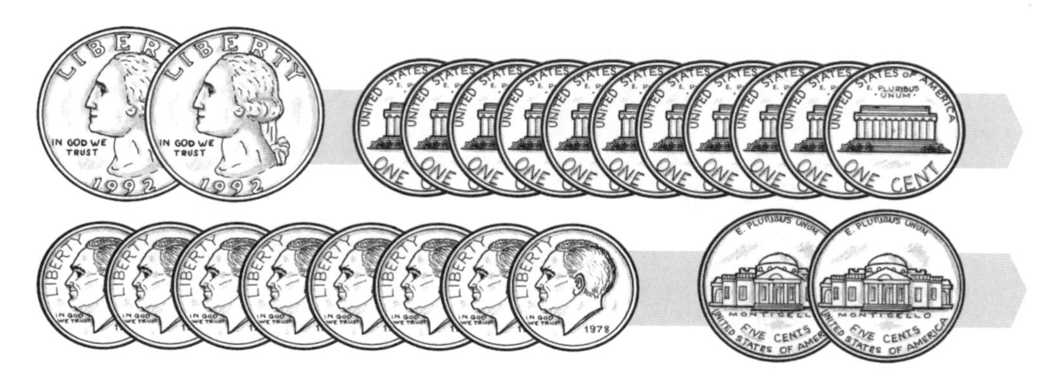

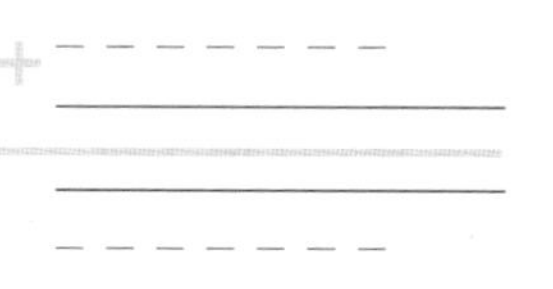

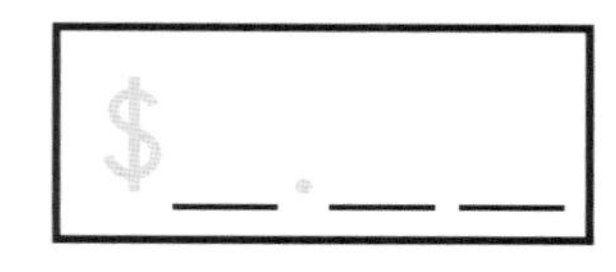

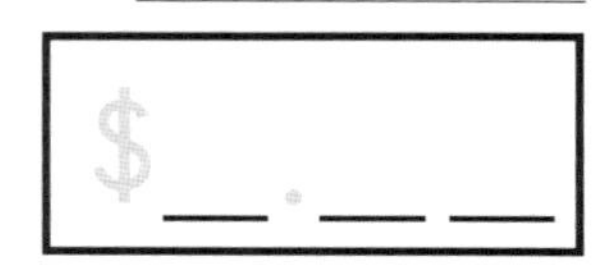

❖ Extra: Can you do this? ❖

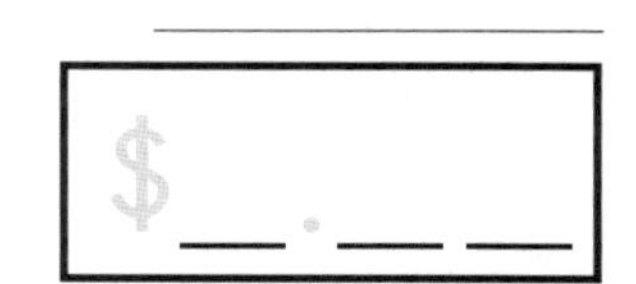

128 **Write a fact and a triplet for each picture.**

Answer these facts.

15	3	14	12	5	9	13	4
− 6	+ 9	− 6	− 7	+ 8	+ 6	− 4	+ 8

5	13	6	8	12	12	15	6
+ 7	− 6	+ 9	+ 6	− 4	− 6	− 9	+ 7

14	12	15	4	13	6	9	6
− 7	− 5	− 6	+ 9	− 5	+ 9	+ 5	+ 6

Answer these problems. Carry or borrow when you need to.

65 + 78	94 − 76	59 + 76	48 + 96	95 − 56	93 − 36
56 + 99	61 − 55	68 + 76	85 − 79	69 + 55	95 − 26
83 − 63	46 + 97	86 + 58	49 + 86	84 − 27	75 − 36

Trace the rule and copy it.

2 pints = 1 quart

____ ________ = ____ ________

Mother put 1 quart of tomato juice into the soup. How many pints was that?

____ ________

128

Answer these problems.

6	3	6	4	8	5	3	3
3	5	2	5	1	2	5	2
+ 5	+ 2	+ 4	+ 2	+ 5	+ 6	+ 5	+ 9
___	___	___	___	___	___	___	___

5	2	2	4	6	1	1	5
4	3	7	1	2	8	3	0
+ 5	+ 8	+ 4	+ 9	+ 3	+ 3	+ 6	+ 9
___	___	___	___	___	___	___	___

Do these number strings.

4 + 6 − 2 + 6 = ___

3 + 4 + 2 + 6 = ___

13 − 4 − 4 + 9 = ___

14 − 7 + 3 − 2 = ___

5 + 6 − 4 + 7 = ___

15 − 6 − 5 + 7 = ___

Measure these lines.

Speed Drill

"Let us run
with patience the race
that is set before us."
Hebrews 12:1

		$7 + 7$	$4 + 8$	$9 + 6$	$4 + 9$	$8 + 6$	$6 + 9$
		$6 + 7$	$6 + 8$	$9 + 5$	$5 + 7$	$6 + 9$	$5 + 8$
$6 + 6$	$9 + 3$	$6 + 9$	$7 + 6$	$6 + 8$	$9 + 6$	$8 + 4$	$9 + 4$
$9 + 6$	$5 + 9$	$8 + 5$	$7 + 5$	$6 + 9$	$3 + 9$	$7 + 7$	$9 + 6$

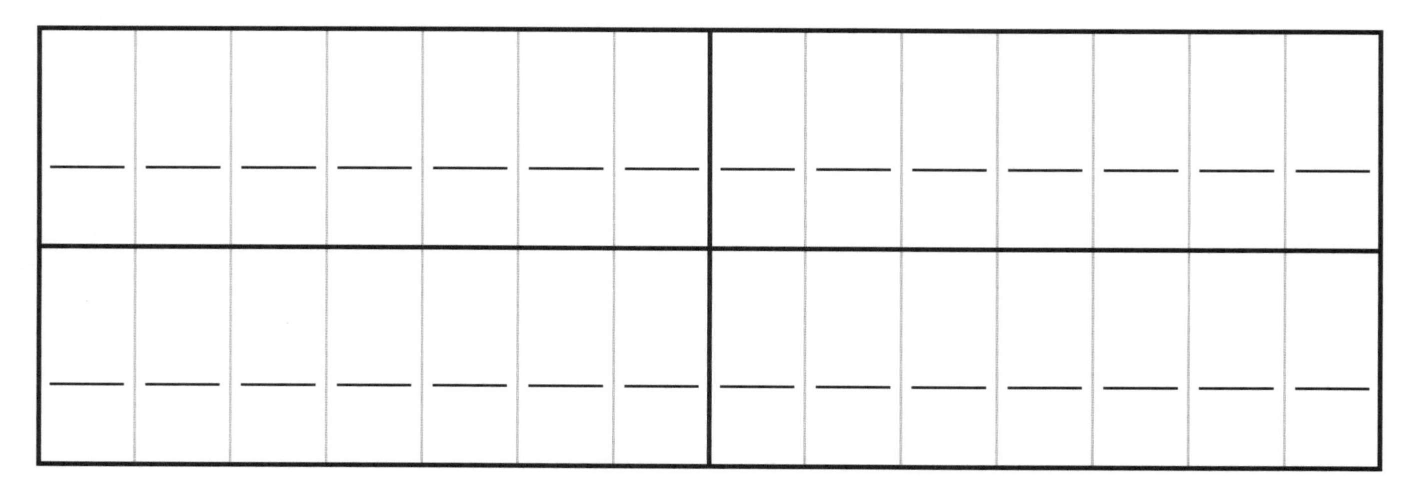

129 Write a fact and a triplet for each picture.

Fill in the missing whole or part.

9 + ___ = 14	15 − ___ = 6	___ + 5 = 14
___ − 6 = 9	___ − 5 = 9	13 − 4 = ___
13 − ___ = 9	___ + 9 = 15	15 − ___ = 9
9 + ___ = 15	14 − 9 = ___	___ + 6 = 15
___ + 4 = 13	___ − 9 = 6	13 − ___ = 9
6 + 9 = ___	6 + ___ = 15	9 + 5 = ___

Answer these facts.

4 + 7	15 − 9	6 + 6	11 − 2	14 − 5	9 + 6	13 − 5	11 − 4
6 + 7	3 + 8	8 + 5	15 − 9	6 + 9	7 + 5	11 − 3	12 − 5
7 + 7	5 + 6	13 − 4	11 − 6				

If it's 1 child on a swing
Or 15 bees on wing,
*"His eye seeth
every precious thing."*
If it's 300 busy ants,
Or 400 tiny plants,
*"His eye seeth
every precious thing."*

Answer these problems. Carry or borrow when you need to.

56 + 99	94 − 55	69 + 74	85 − 76	84 − 27	66 + 57
56 + 58	85 − 66	29 + 86	94 − 78	59 + 55	92 − 73
75 − 36	89 + 66	63 − 54	47 + 96	85 + 38	93 − 36

129

There are five minutes between each number and the next. Count the minutes by 5's, and write the time.

10:15

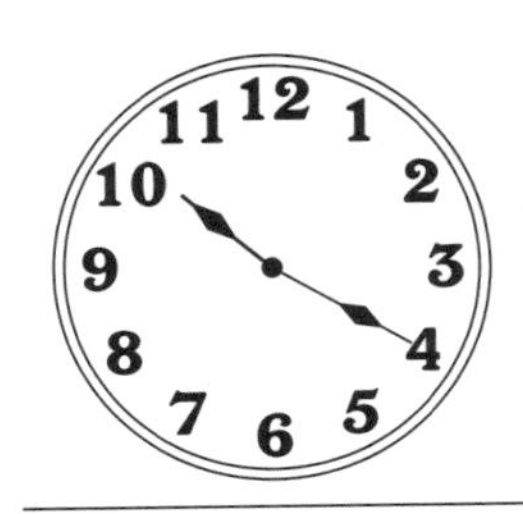

Write the time.

Answer the story problem.

Lois counted fifteen jars on a shelf. Six jars had beans in them. The rest had peaches. How many jars had peaches?

Trace and finish the rule.

2 cups = ______ ____________

2 pints = ______ ____________

Answer these problems. Be careful!

1. Mary opened 1 quart of peaches for supper.

That is the same as ______ ____________.

2. Mother opened 1 pint of relish for supper.

That is the same as ______ ____________.

3. The family used 2 whole cups of ketchup on their hamburgers!

That is the same as ______ ____________.

4. The macaroni salad left from supper filled 2 pint containers.

That is the same as ______ ____________.

Draw lines of the correct length. Start at the dot.

$3\frac{1}{2}$" •

5" •

$1\frac{1}{2}$" •

6" •

$4\frac{1}{2}$" •

130 Write all the 11's–15's triplets that you have learned.

11	12	13
◯ ___ ___	◯ ___ ___	◯ ___ ___
◯ ___ ___	◯ ___ ___	◯ ___ ___
◯ ___ ___	◯ ___ ___	◯ ___ ___
◯ ___ ___	◯ ___ ___	

14	15
◯ ___ ___	◯ ___ ___
◯ ___ ___	
◯ ___ ___	

Answer these facts.

13	11	8	10	9	13	8	15
- 6	- 2	+ 6	- 2	+ 5	- 4	+ 6	- 9
___	___	___	___	___	___	___	___

11	14	4	4	10	13
- 4	- 7	+ 6	+ 8	- 5	- 5
___	___	___	___	___	___

If it's 1 child on a swing, / Or 15 bees on wing, / *"His eye seeth every precious thing."*
If it's 300 busy ants, / Or 400 tiny plants, / *"His eye seeth every precious thing."*

Answer these addition problems. Carry when you need to.

44	63	55	72	43	34
22	34	22	23	23	32
+ 36	+ 42	+ 67	+ 34	+ 49	+ 55

33	54	56	53	42	43
42	32	33	21	46	42
+ 45	+ 63	+ 65	+ 65	+ 63	+ 27

Write the time.

Answer these story problems.

Miriam was busy cleaning for Mother. In the living room she picked up 14 blocks and 10 toy animals. In the kitchen she picked up 11 baby toys. How many toys did Miriam pick up?

85 ants get into a beehive. 67 more ants are coming to the hive. How many ants is that altogether?

100¢ is the same as $1.00

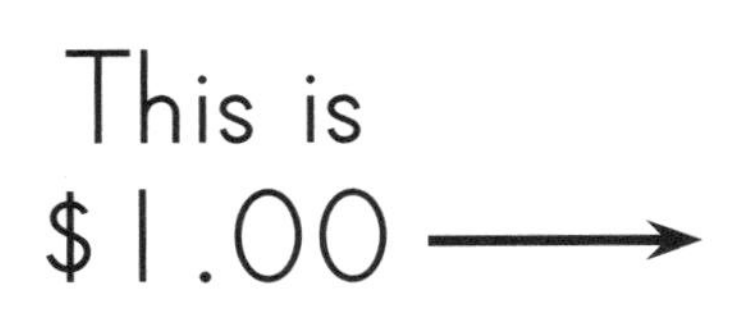

Count the dollars and dimes. Write the amount.

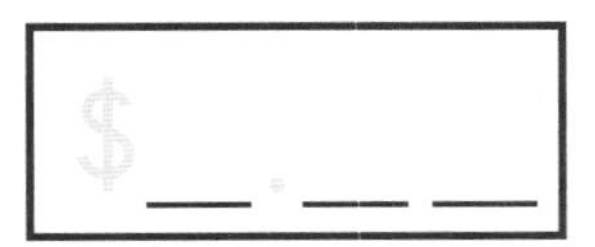

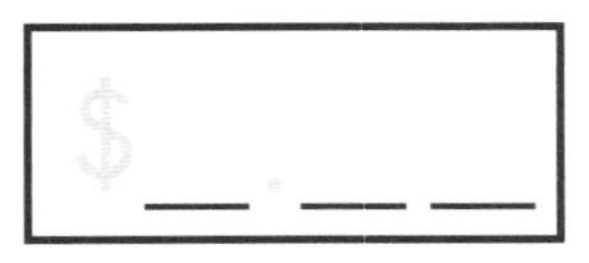

Mother used one dollar and two dimes to buy celery.

Father has one dollar and 8 dimes in his pocket.

The clerk gave Mr. Sams one dollar and 5 dimes.

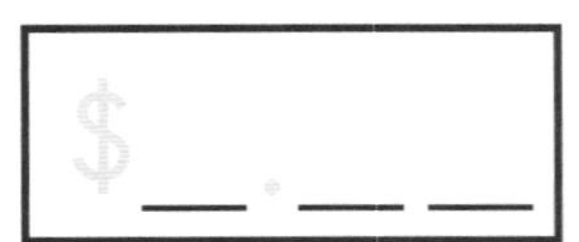

Speed Drill

130

"Let us run
with patience the race
that is set before us."
Hebrews 12:1

15	12	14	13	15	12
- 6	- 4	- 6	- 4	- 9	- 9

14	14	12	15	13	14
- 5	- 8	- 8	- 6	- 6	- 7

14	15	13	12	14	13	15	12
- 9	- 6	- 8	- 3	- 6	- 5	- 9	- 7

14	12	14	15	13	15	12	13
- 7	- 6	- 9	- 9	- 7	- 6	- 5	- 9

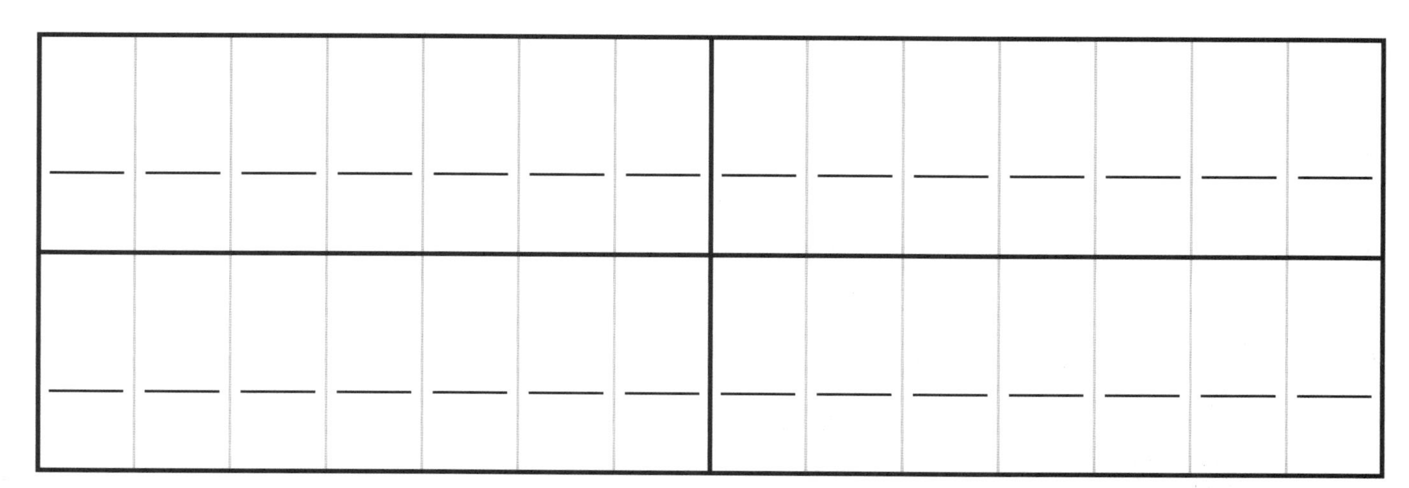

Fill in the whole and the parts.

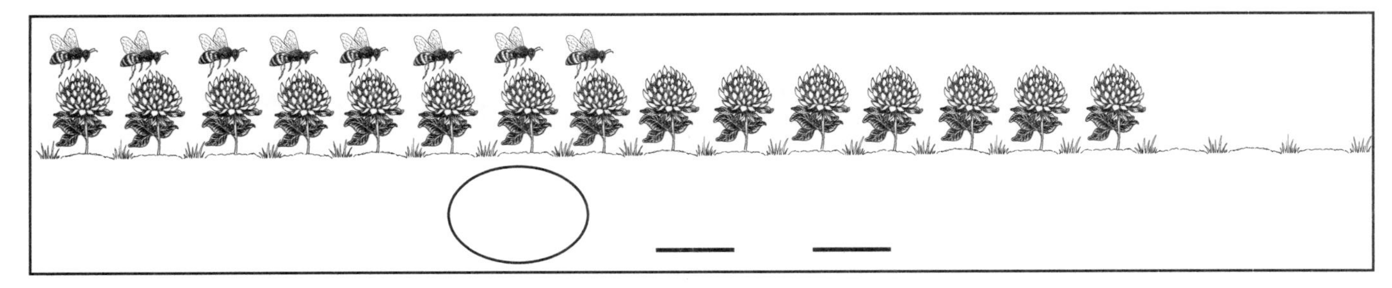

Write a fact for each picture.

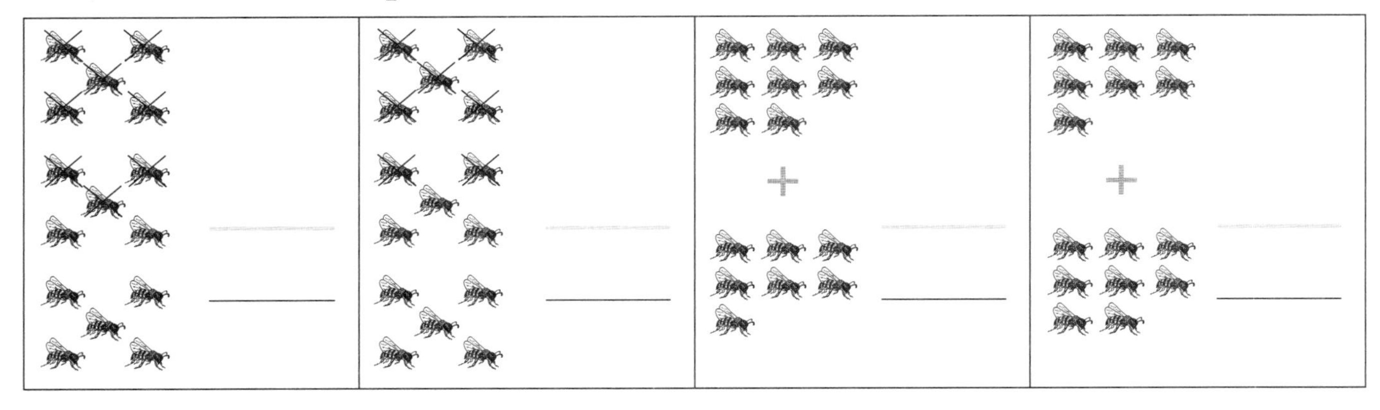

Trace and copy the triplet. Write the facts twice in the hives.

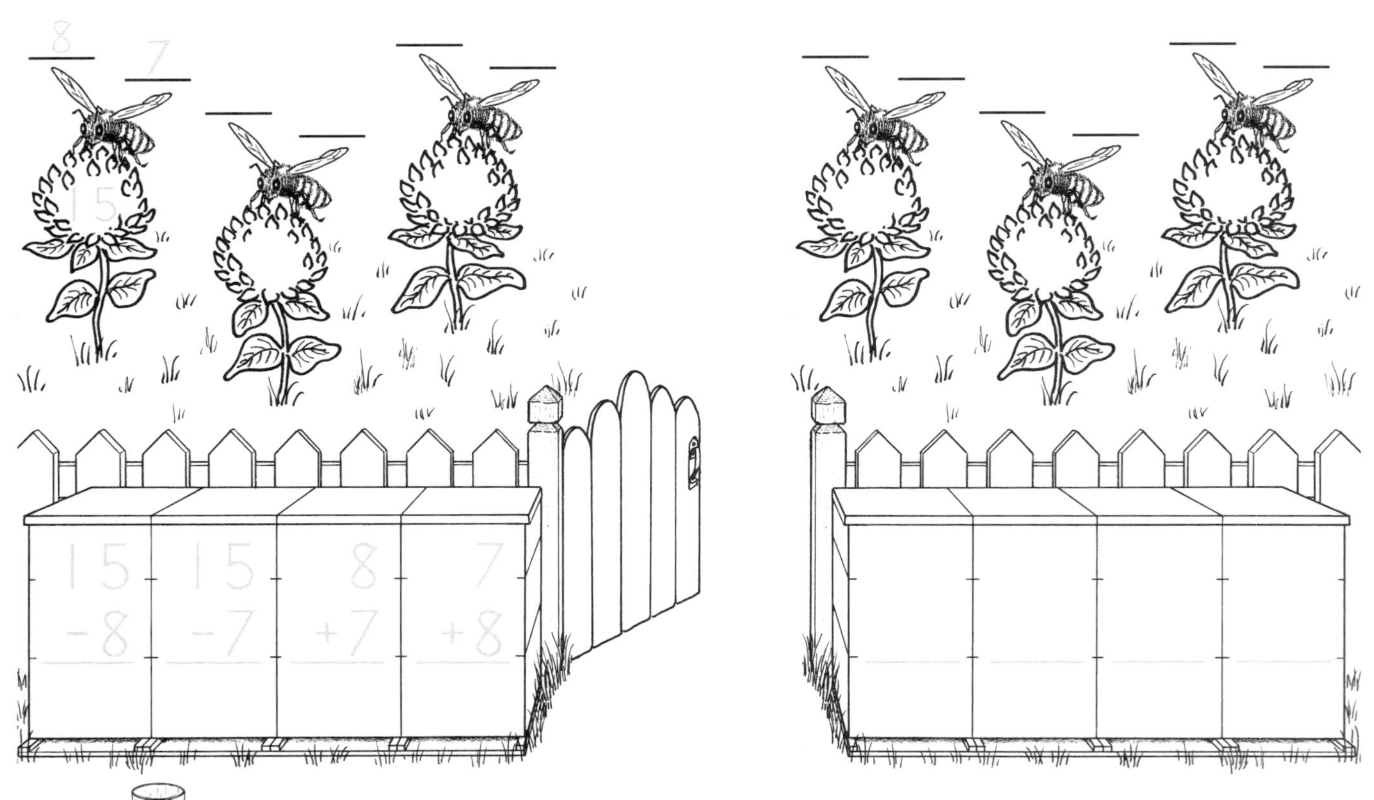

"The LORD shall bring thee into the land . . . flowing with milk and honey."

Exodus 13:5

Answer these facts.

8	15	14	7	15	15	8	7
+ 7	− 8	− 9	+ 8	− 6	− 7	+ 7	+ 8
15	7	8	5	15	15	6	15
− 8	+ 8	+ 7	+ 9	− 7	− 8	+ 9	− 7
14	15	7	9	15	8	15	7
− 5	− 7	+ 8	+ 6	− 8	+ 7	− 8	+ 8

If it's 1 child on a swing
Or 15 bees on wing,
*"His eye seeth
every precious thing."*
If it's 300 busy ants,
Or 400 tiny plants,
*"His eye seeth
every precious thing."*

15	8	9	15
− 9	+ 7	+ 5	− 7

Answer these problems. Borrow when you need to.

93	85	99	84	95	87
−77	−37	−69	−68	−47	−57
83	99	95	92	88	84
−44	−35	−66	−53	−24	−55

131 Write the time.

______ ______ ______ ______ ______

______ ______ ______ ______ ______

______ ______ ______ ______ ______

______ ______ ______ ______ ______

Count the money. Write the amount.

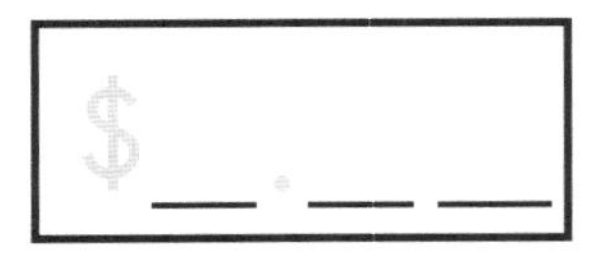

Do these number strings.

$5 + 3 + 6 - 5 =$ ___

$2 + 7 + 6 - 8 =$ ___

$14 - 6 + 1 - 6 =$ ___

$10 - 7 + 5 + 3 =$ ___

$7 + 6 - 4 - 2 =$ ___

$12 - 5 - 5 + 9 =$ ___

Answer these story problems.

Fred's pet duck has one dozen eggs in her nest. Today 5 eggs hatched. How many eggs did not hatch yet?

_____ _______________

_____ _______________

_____ _______________

Father pays 56¢ for a pencil and 89¢ for a pen. How many cents does Father pay for both things?

____

____

____

$__.__ __

Write the digits in the correct places.

	thousands	hundreds	tens	ones
1,506				
3,084				
1,720				
6,905				
4,017				
2,860				
5,900				

132

Fill in the whole and the parts.

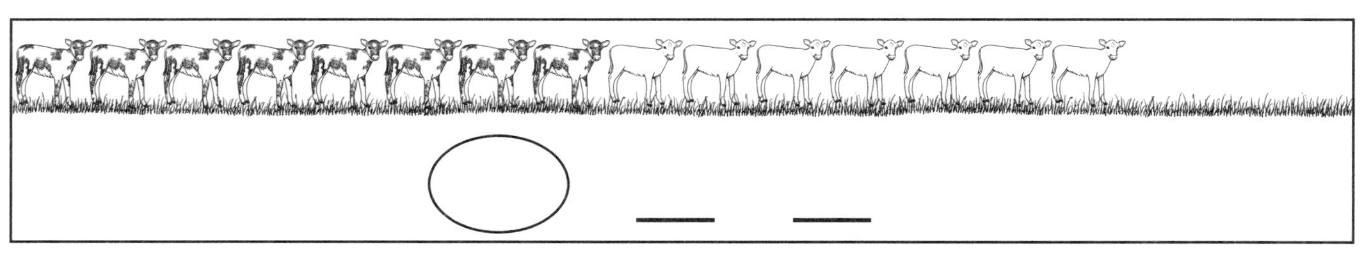

Answer the facts. Make the pictures fit the facts.

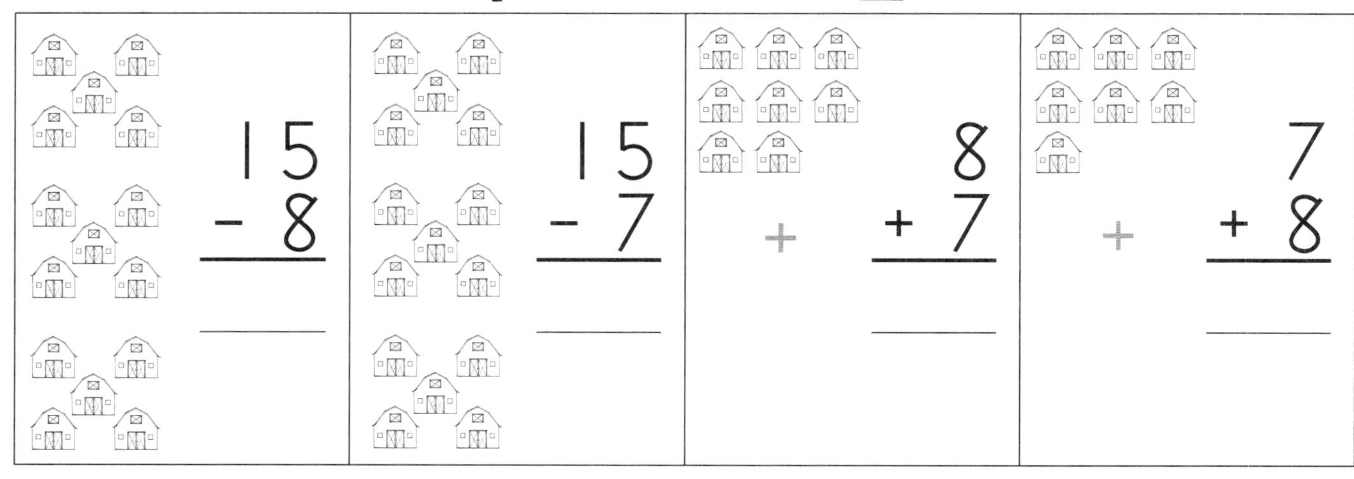

15 − 8 = ___	15 − 7 = ___	8 + 7 = ___	7 + 8 = ___

Trace and copy the triplet.

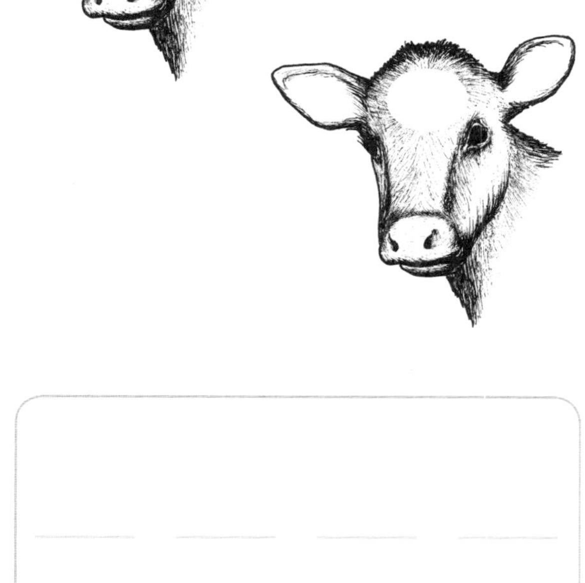

Write the four facts twice.

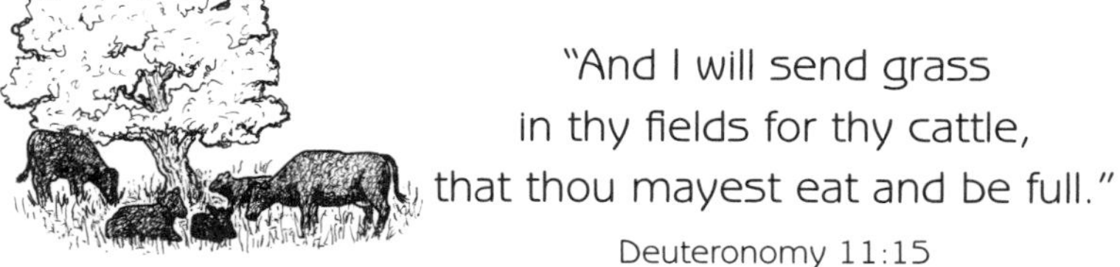

"And I will send grass
in thy fields for thy cattle,
that thou mayest eat and be full."
Deuteronomy 11:15

Answer these facts.

132

15 − 7	7 + 7	15 − 8	6 + 8	8 + 7	15 − 7	14 − 8	7 + 8
8 + 7	14 − 7	6 + 8	15 − 7	8 + 6	7 + 7	8 + 7	7 + 8
14 − 7	15 − 8	8 + 6	8 + 7	14 − 6	7 + 8	15 − 7	7 + 8
15 − 7	14 − 6	15 − 8	7 + 7	8 + 7	14 − 8	7 + 8	15 − 8

Answer these story problems.

Galen is 15 years old, and Ray is 9 years old. How much less is Ray's age than Galen's age?

_____ _______________

_____ _______________

_____ _______________

In Mr. Roger's store, a banana cost 40¢ and an apple cost 59¢. How much less did the banana cost?

____

____

____

132 Answer these addition problems. Carry when you need to.

578	337	266	443	351
+367	+367	+529	+385	+449
485	547	349	256	168
+268	+368	+355	+497	+747
268	267	532	359	454
+436	+678	+296	+436	+299

Write the time.

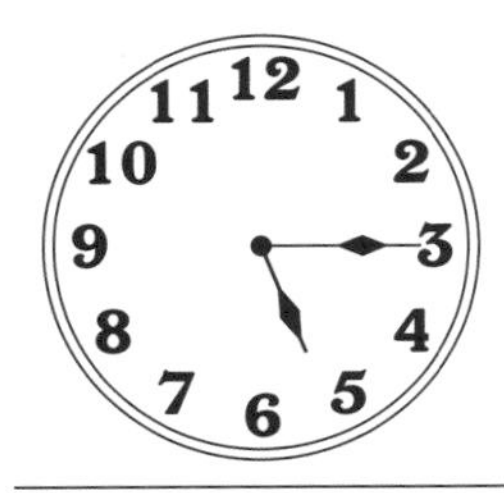

Speed Drill

132

"Let us run
with patience the race
that is set before us."
Hebrews 12:1

8	14	15	8	15	7
+ 7	− 8	− 7	+ 7	− 8	+ 8

15	8	15	8	14	7
− 7	+ 7	− 8	+ 6	− 6	+ 8

15	15	8	8	14	15	6	8
− 8	− 7	+ 6	+ 7	− 8	− 8	+ 8	+ 7

6	15	7	8	15	14	7	8
+ 8	− 8	+ 8	+ 7	− 7	− 6	+ 8	+ 6

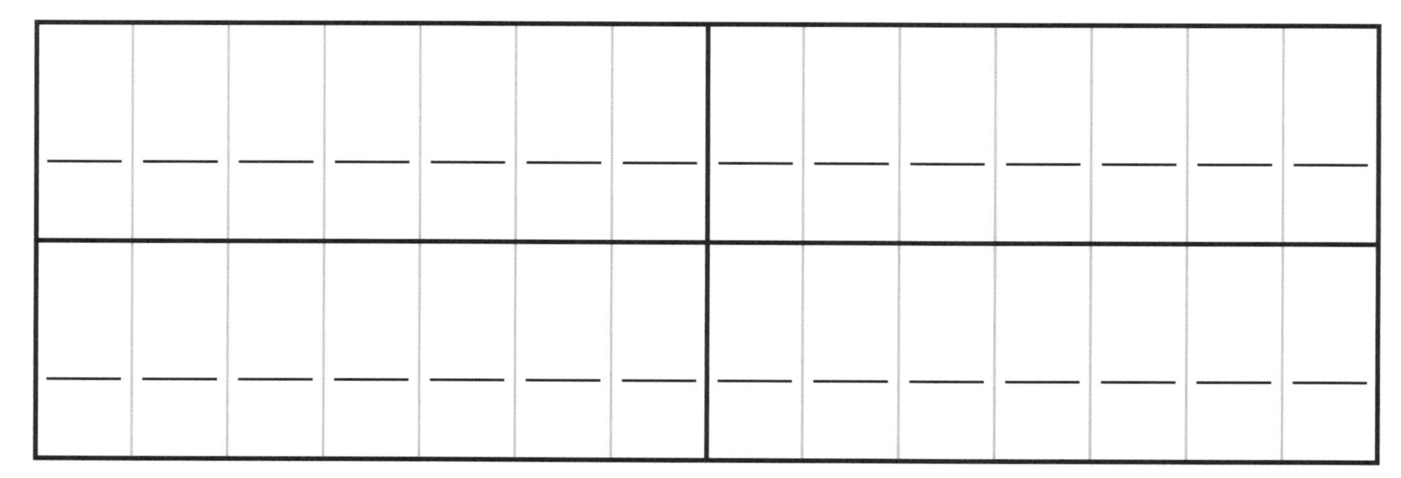

133 Fill in the whole and the parts. Write the facts.

___ ___ ___ ___

___ ___ ___ ___

( ) ___ ___

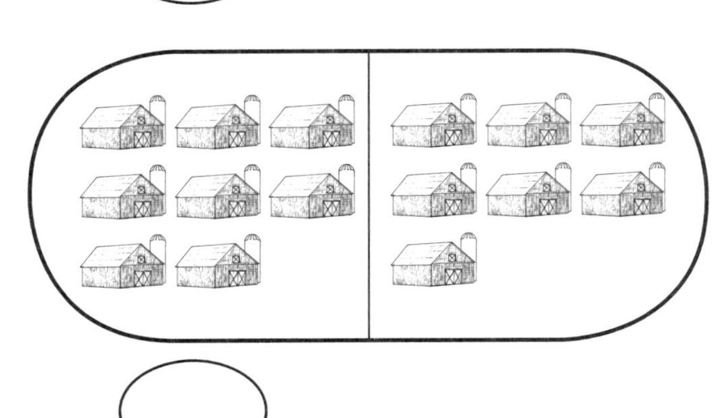

___ ___ ___ ___

___ ___ ___ ___

( ) ___ ___

Fill in the missing whole or part.

15 − 8 = ___	7 + ___ = 14	8 + ___ = 15
15 − ___ = 8	___ − 8 = 7	14 − ___ = 7
8 + 6 = ___	8 + ___ = 14	___ − 6 = 8
___ + 7 = 15	___ + 8 = 15	15 − ___ = 7
14 − ___ = 8	6 + ___ = 14	6 + 8 = ___
7 + 8 = ___	15 − 7 = ___	___ + 7 = 14

Answer these problems. Carry when you need to.

98	71	77	158	127	73
− 13	+ 49	+ 28	− 74	− 65	+ 58
50	56	146	159	84	155
+ 70	+ 49	− 62	− 97	+ 47	− 70
68	157	135	70	139	47
+ 37	− 73	− 73	+ 61	− 54	+ 38

Answer these story problems.

Balak offered 14 animals on an altar. Seven animals were bullocks, and the rest were rams. How many of the animals were rams?

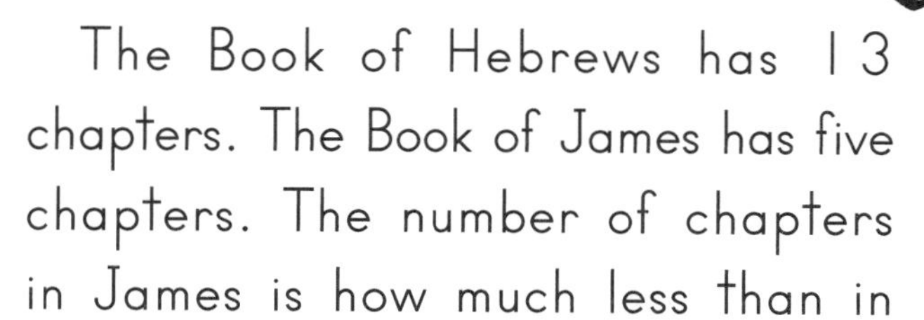

The Book of Hebrews has 13 chapters. The Book of James has five chapters. The number of chapters in James is how much less than in Hebrews?

133 **Do these number strings.**

3 + 1 + 2 + 2 + 4 = ___

4 + 2 + 1 + 5 − 3 = ___

2 + 3 + 3 + 2 − 5 = ___

5 + 2 + 2 + 5 − 6 = ___

14 − 8 + 3 + 2 − 3 = ___

15 − 9 + 2 + 5 − 4 = ___

Trace the rule and copy it.

3 feet = 1 yard

___ ______ = ___ ______

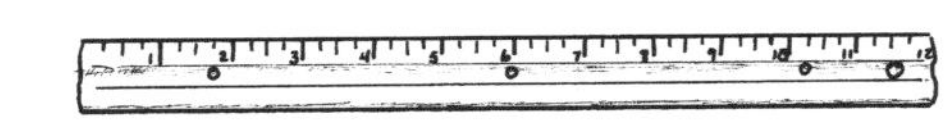  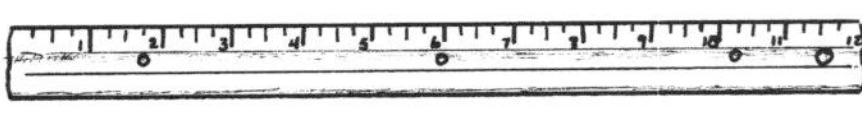

Trace and finish the rules.

7 days = ___ ______

12 months = ___ ______

"And Jacob said unto Pharaoh,
The days of the years of my pilgrimage are an hundred and thirty **years**."

Genesis 47:9

Do you know how many months that is? In 130 years, there are 1,560 months.

Count the money. Add the amounts.

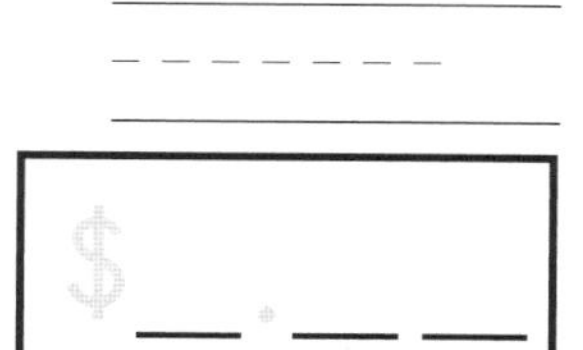

$ __ . __ __

❖ Extra: Can you do these? ❖

Circle the correct answers.

1. Are 4 **quarters** and 1 **dime** the same as $1.00? yes no
2. Are 3 **quarters** and 5 **nickels** the same as $1.00? yes no
3. Are 9 **dimes** and 2 **nickels** the same as $1.00? yes no
4. Are 9 **dimes** and 8 **pennies** the same as $1.00? yes no

134 Fill in the whole and the parts. Write the facts.

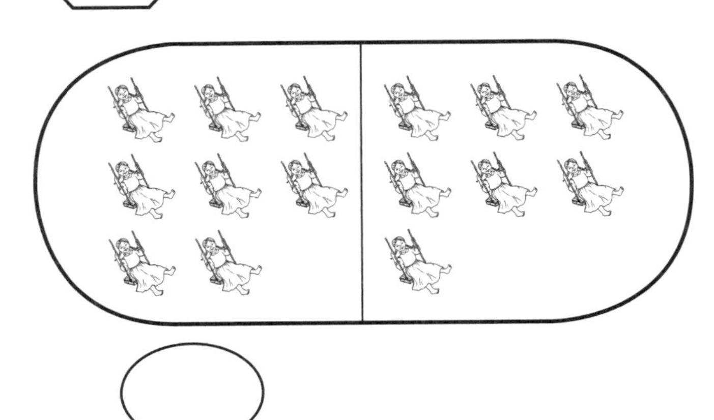

Answer these facts.

14 − 5	15 − 7	7 + 6	15 − 6	8 + 5	6 + 8	15 − 8	3 + 9
12 − 8	8 + 7	13 − 6	15 − 8	8 + 6	13 − 4	15 − 9	7 + 7
5 + 7	14 − 9	9 + 4	7 + 8	14 − 6	15 − 7	9 + 5	12 − 3
8 + 7	12 − 5	15 − 7	13 − 5	6 + 9	14 − 7	8 + 7	14 − 8

Answer these addition problems. Carry when you need to. Use commas when you need to.

735	363	725	893	674
+827	+477	+688	+366	+229
954	466	521	832	577
+617	+388	+479	+739	+277
418	562	856	584	824
+485	+697	+557	+256	+738

Write the time.

God, make my life a little flower that giveth joy to all;
Content to bloom in native bower although its place be small.

—*Matilda B. B. Edwards*

134 Do these number strings.

$3 + 5 + 7 - 9 + 2 =$ ___

$2 + 3 + 4 + 5 - 7 =$ ___

$10 - 7 + 1 + 5 + 6 =$ ___

$6 + 6 - 4 + 5 - 4 =$ ___

$14 - 8 + 2 + 3 - 4 =$ ___

$13 - 9 + 2 + 2 + 7 =$ ___

Write a fraction for the shaded part of each shape.

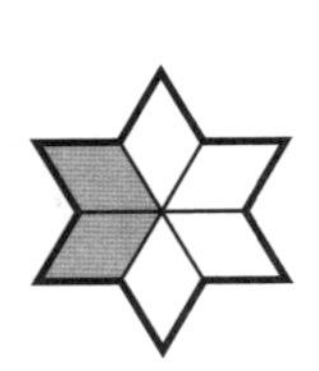 ___

 ___

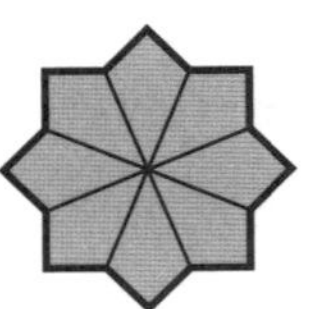 ___

 ___

 ___

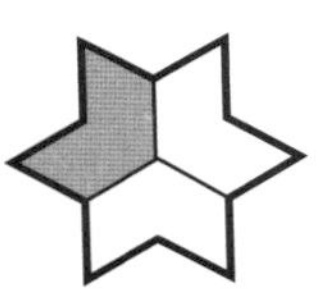 ___

 ___

 ___

 ___

 ___

 ___

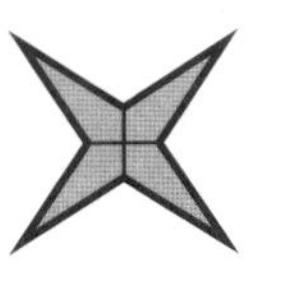 ___

Trace and finish the rule.

___ ___ = 1 yard

Speed Drill

"Let us run
with patience the race
that is set before us."

Hebrews 12:1

$7 + 8 =$ ___ $8 + 6 =$ ___ $15 - 8 =$ ___ $15 - 7 =$ ___ $6 + 9 =$ ___ $15 - 9 =$ ___

$7 + 7 =$ ___ $15 - 8 =$ ___ $9 + 6 =$ ___ $14 - 6 =$ ___ $15 - 7 =$ ___ $8 + 7 =$ ___

$15 - 9 =$ ___ $7 + 8 =$ ___ $15 - 8 =$ ___ $7 + 7 =$ ___ $15 - 6 =$ ___ $6 + 8 =$ ___ $15 - 7 =$ ___ $8 + 7 =$ ___

$15 - 7 =$ ___ $8 + 7 =$ ___ $14 - 8 =$ ___ $6 + 9 =$ ___ $14 - 7 =$ ___ $7 + 8 =$ ___ $15 - 8 =$ ___ $14 - 7 =$ ___

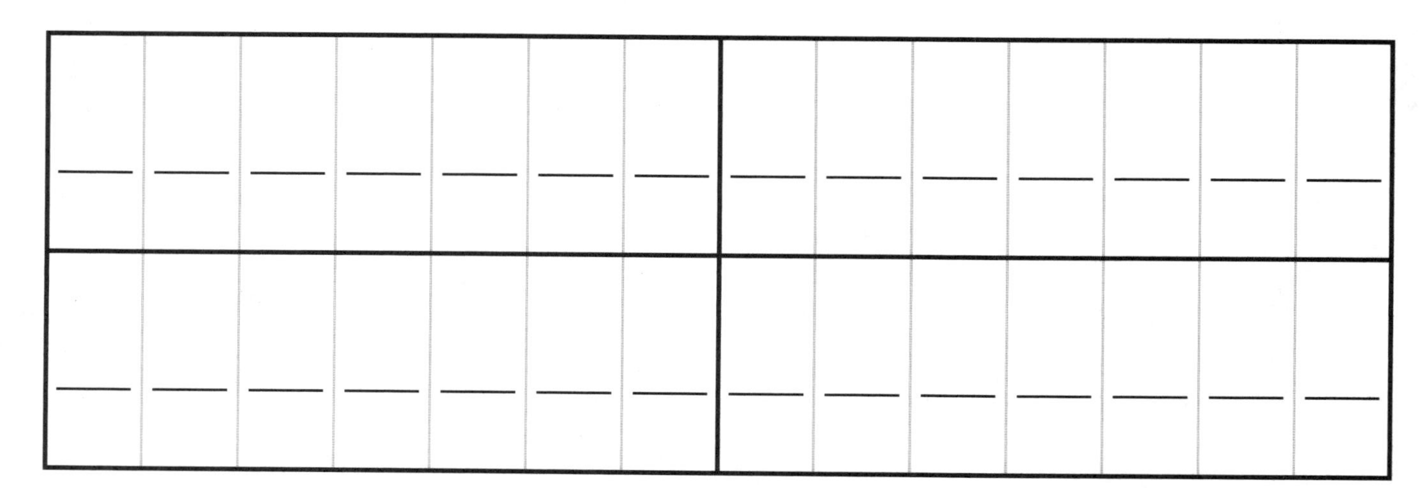

135 Write a fact and a triplet for each picture.

+

+

Answer these facts.

13	15	5	15	11	8	7	12
− 4	− 6	+ 6	− 7	− 2	+ 5	+ 8	− 5

11	14	6	8	3	14	9	15
− 4	− 5	+ 7	+ 7	+ 8	− 7	+ 6	− 7

6	9	7	12	7	15	9	13
+ 6	+ 4	+ 8	− 6	+ 7	− 8	+ 3	− 7

Answer these problems. Carry or borrow when you need to.

78 +67	77 +76	94 −59	95 −68	67 +58	93 −35
84 −17	47 +98	91 −53	95 −28	66 +79	85 −47
85 −58	74 −38	85 +68	67 +78	85 −27	76 +49

If it's 1 child on a swing or 15 bees on wing,
"His eye seeth every precious thing."
If it's 300 busy ants, or 400 tiny plants,
"His eye seeth every precious thing."

Answer these story problems.

Yesterday Jason carefully did his math lesson in 31 minutes. Today he finished in 15 minutes. How much less time did Jason take today?

When Sister Ruth checked the lessons, Jason got 95 percent on the first lesson but only 78 percent today. What was the difference in his scores?

135

Answer these problems.

4	7	4	5	6	7	2	7
4	2	3	4	1	2	6	0
+ 7	+ 5	+ 8	+ 3	+ 4	+ 4	+ 4	+ 8
____	____	____	____	____	____	____	____

3	3	5	6	3	4	5	3
5	4	2	2	3	2	3	5
+ 6	+ 8	+ 5	+ 7	+ 7	+ 5	+ 7	+ 4
____	____	____	____	____	____	____	____

Measure these screwdrivers and screws.

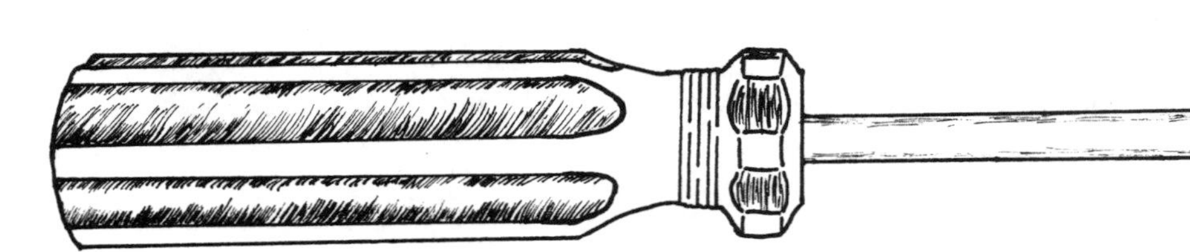

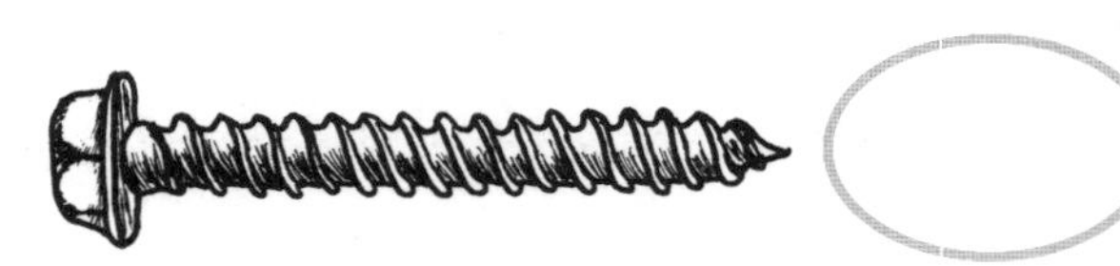

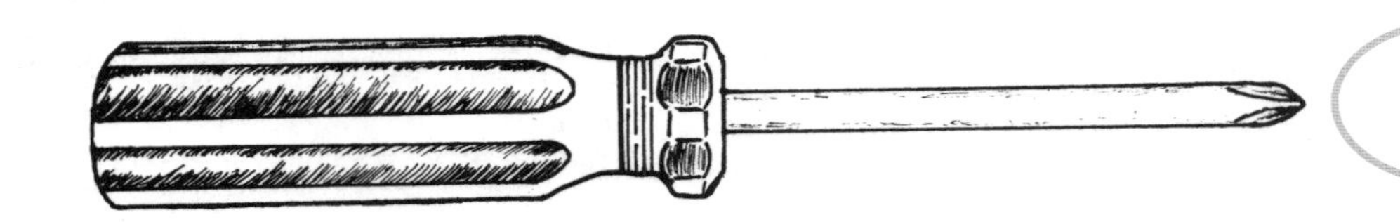

Count the money. Write the amount.

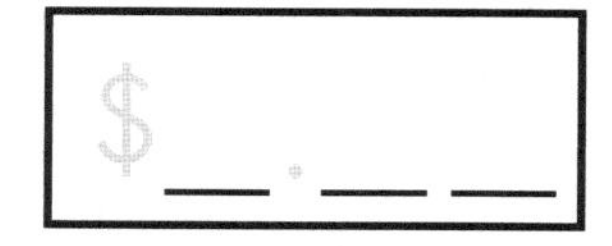

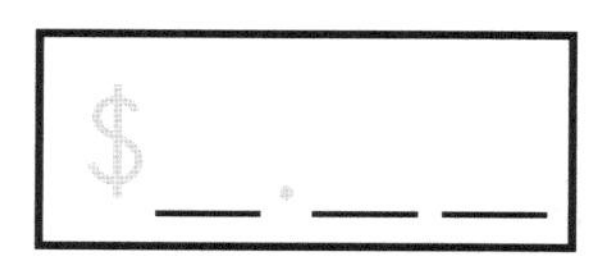

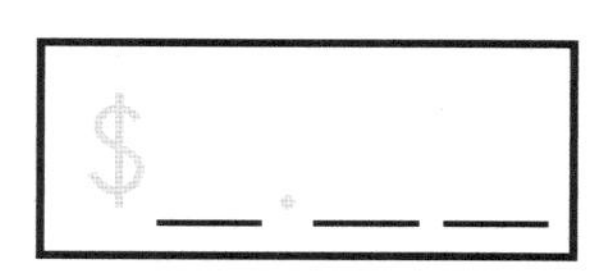

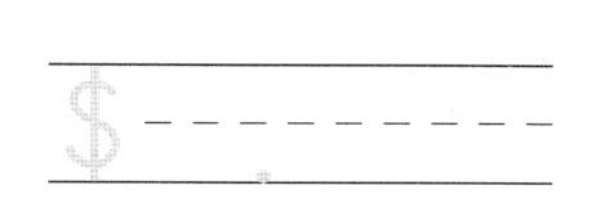

+ $

$ ___ . ___ ___

Answer these questions.

1. If Mother has 2 **quarters and 1 dime**, can she buy a head of broccoli that costs 65¢? ________
2. If Big Sister has **one dollar and 1 dime**, can she buy a pen that costs $1.20? ________
3. Father has **one dollar and 3 dimes**. Can he buy the pen? ________

136 Write all the 11's–15's triplets that you have learned.

11	12	13
◯ ___ ___	◯ ___ ___	◯ ___ ___
◯ ___ ___	◯ ___ ___	◯ ___ ___
◯ ___ ___	◯ ___ ___	◯ ___ ___
◯ ___ ___	◯ ___ ___	

14	15
◯ ___ ___	◯ ___ ___
◯ ___ ___	◯ ___ ___
◯ ___ ___	

Answer these facts.

4	8	6	4	15	9	4	13
+ 7	+ 4	+ 8	+ 9	− 8	+ 6	+ 6	− 6
___	___	___	___	___	___	___	___

11	5	12	15	5	8	10	3
− 3	+ 9	− 4	− 6	+ 8	+ 7	− 2	+ 9
___	___	___	___	___	___	___	___

"Pleasant words are as an honeycomb, sweet to the soul, and health to the bones."

Proverbs 16:24

Answer these problems. Carry or borrow when you need to.

65	47	85	64	35	64
- 8	+ 18	- 7	- 5	- 9	- 7

87	90	56	68	73	47
+ 48	- 43	+ 79	+ 66	- 66	+ 87

62	64	95	95	26	95
- 55	- 38	- 36	- 17	+ 39	- 38

Answer these story problems.

Yesterday Jason hurried too much and did his math lesson in 15 minutes. Sister Ruth asked him to do his lesson again. This time it took 25 minutes. How much time did Jason spend on that lesson altogether?

God sent a wind. It did what we could not do. It blew down seven trees in the woods. It blew down eight trees in the field. How many trees was that?

Aunt Mary lives 45 miles from our house. Grandpa's live 37 miles from our house. How many more miles is it to Aunt Mary's than to Grandpa's?

136 Write the time.

Trace and finish the rules. Trace to finish the sentence.

_____ ____________ = 1 pint

_____ ____________ = 1 quart

This jug holds 1 gallon.

Speed Drill

"Let us run
with patience the race
that is set before us."

Hebrews 12:1

8	6	4	4	6	8
+ 7	+ 6	+ 9	+ 8	+ 9	+ 3

4	9	5	7	5	6
+ 7	+ 6	+ 8	+ 8	+ 7	+ 8

8	6	7	2	7	5	6	5
+ 7	+ 7	+ 8	+ 9	+ 7	+ 6	+ 9	+ 9

6	2	7	5	2	6	4	3
2	7	1	4	5	3	3	5
+ 6	+ 3	+ 5	+ 6	+ 6	+ 5	+ 5	+ 7

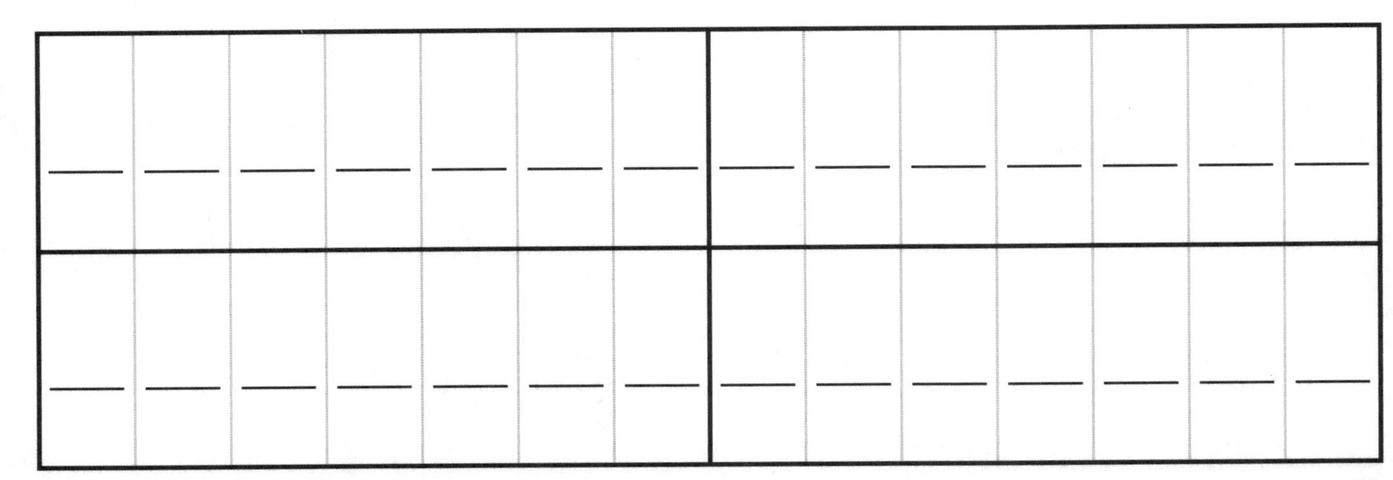

137 This is Addition Family 15. Trace it.

$$\begin{array}{r} 5 \\ +10 \\ \hline 15 \end{array} \quad \begin{array}{r} 6 \\ +9 \\ \hline 15 \end{array} \quad \begin{array}{r} 7 \\ +8 \\ \hline 15 \end{array} \quad \begin{array}{r} 8 \\ +7 \\ \hline 15 \end{array} \quad \begin{array}{r} 9 \\ +6 \\ \hline 15 \end{array} \quad \begin{array}{r} 10 \\ +5 \\ \hline 15 \end{array}$$

Copy the Addition Family 15.

Write a fact for each picture.

+

+

Fill in the missing whole or part.
Watch for the Families 14 and 15 facts!

$$\begin{array}{r} 6 \\ + \\ \hline 15 \end{array} \quad \begin{array}{r} \\ +5 \\ \hline 15 \end{array} \quad \begin{array}{r} 7 \\ + \\ \hline 14 \end{array} \quad \begin{array}{r} 8 \\ +7 \\ \hline \end{array} \quad \begin{array}{r} 10 \\ + \\ \hline 15 \end{array} \quad \begin{array}{r} \\ +9 \\ \hline 14 \end{array} \quad \begin{array}{r} 10 \\ +4 \\ \hline \end{array} \quad \begin{array}{r} 7 \\ + \\ \hline 15 \end{array}$$

Answer these addition facts.

2 + 9	6 + 9	1 + 9	5 + 10	5 + 6	3 + 9	3 + 6	10 + 4
8 + 4	9 + 4	3 + 7	8 + 7	3 + 8	5 + 9	4 + 5	10 + 5
6 + 6	2 + 7	6 + 8	5 + 10	4 + 7	8 + 5	4 + 8	9 + 6
8 + 7	10 + 5	5 + 5	8 + 3	5 + 7	7 + 7	7 + 8	6 + 7

Answer these addition problems. Carry when you need to. Remember the commas.

413 + 297	668 + 627	553 + 896	634 + 347	778 + 274
936 + 359	522 + 188	687 + 662	555 + 497	815 + 166

137 Count the money. Write the amount.

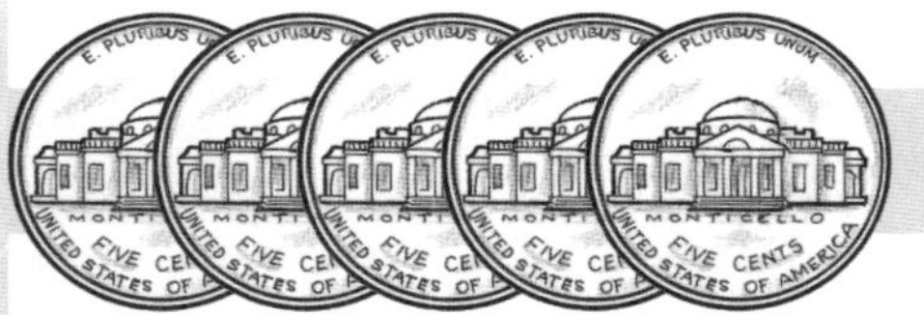
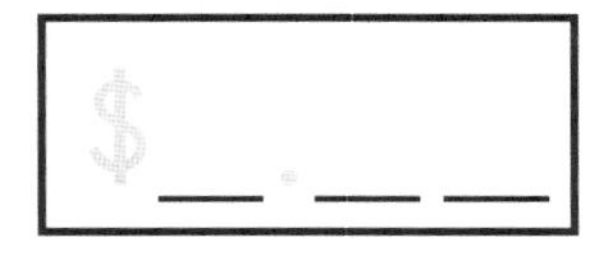

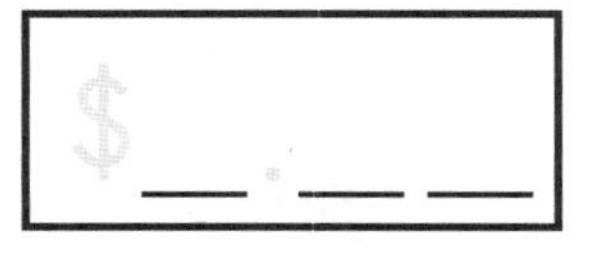

Write the time.

Answer the story problem.

Thirteen kites fly up into the sky. Then 5 kites drop to the ground. How many kites are still sailing in the breeze?

Trace and finish the rule. Copy it below.

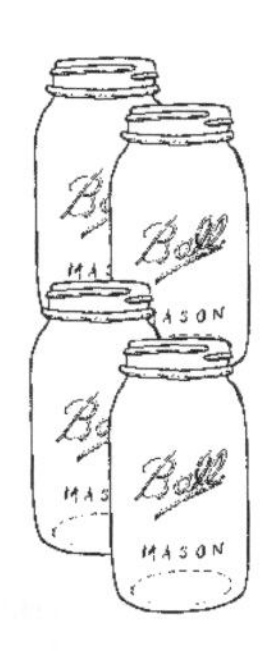

4 quarts = _____ __________

_____ __________ = _____ __________

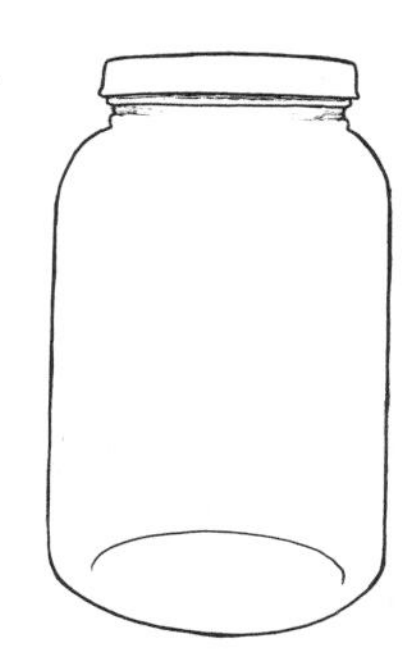

Trace and finish the rules.

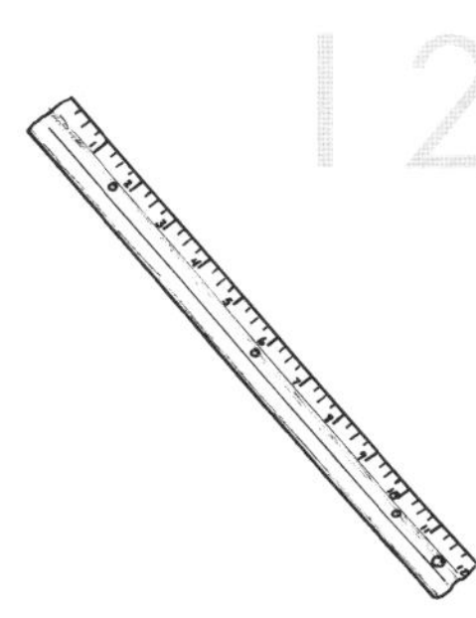

12 inches = _____ __________

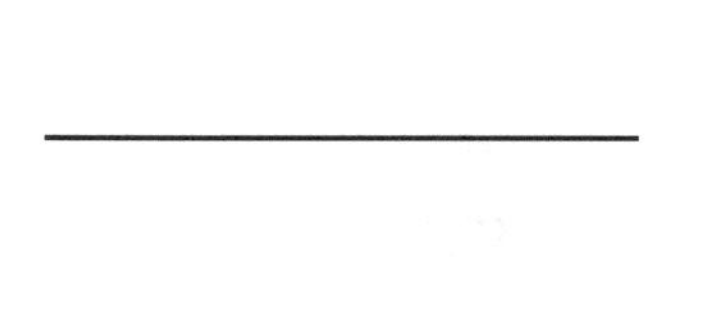

3 feet = _____ __________

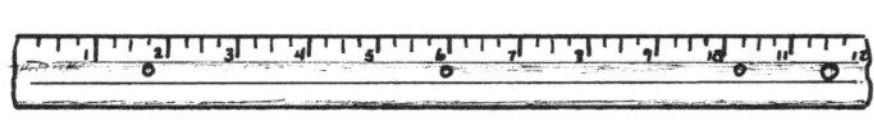 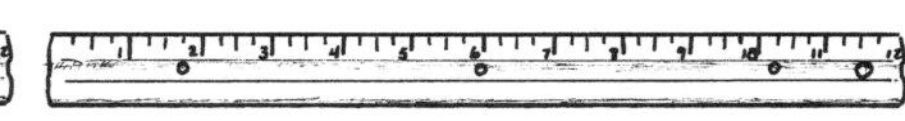 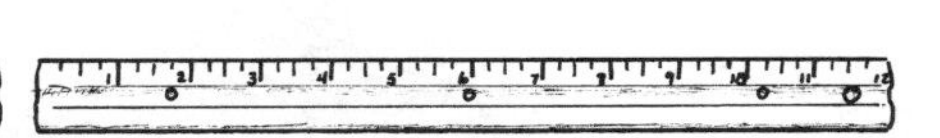

January						
Sunday	Monday	Tuesday	Wednesday	Thursday	Friday	Saturday
			1	2	3	4
5	6	7	8	9	10	11
12	13	14	15	16	17	18
19	20	21	22	23	24	25
26	27	28	29	30	31	

7 days = _____ __________

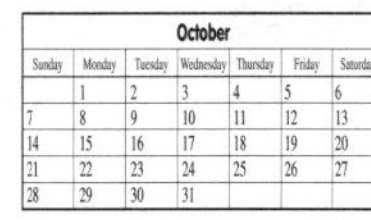

October						
Sunday	Monday	Tuesday	Wednesday	Thursday	Friday	Saturday
	1	2	3	4	5	6
7	8	9	10	11	12	13
14	15	16	17	18	19	20
21	22	23	24	25	26	27
28	29	30	31			

12 months = _____ __________

2 cups = _____ __________

2 pints = _____ __________

138

This is Subtraction Family 15. Trace it.

15	15	15	15	15	15
- 5	- 6	- 7	- 8	- 9	-10
10	9	8	7	6	5

Copy the Subtraction Family 15.

Write a fact for each picture.

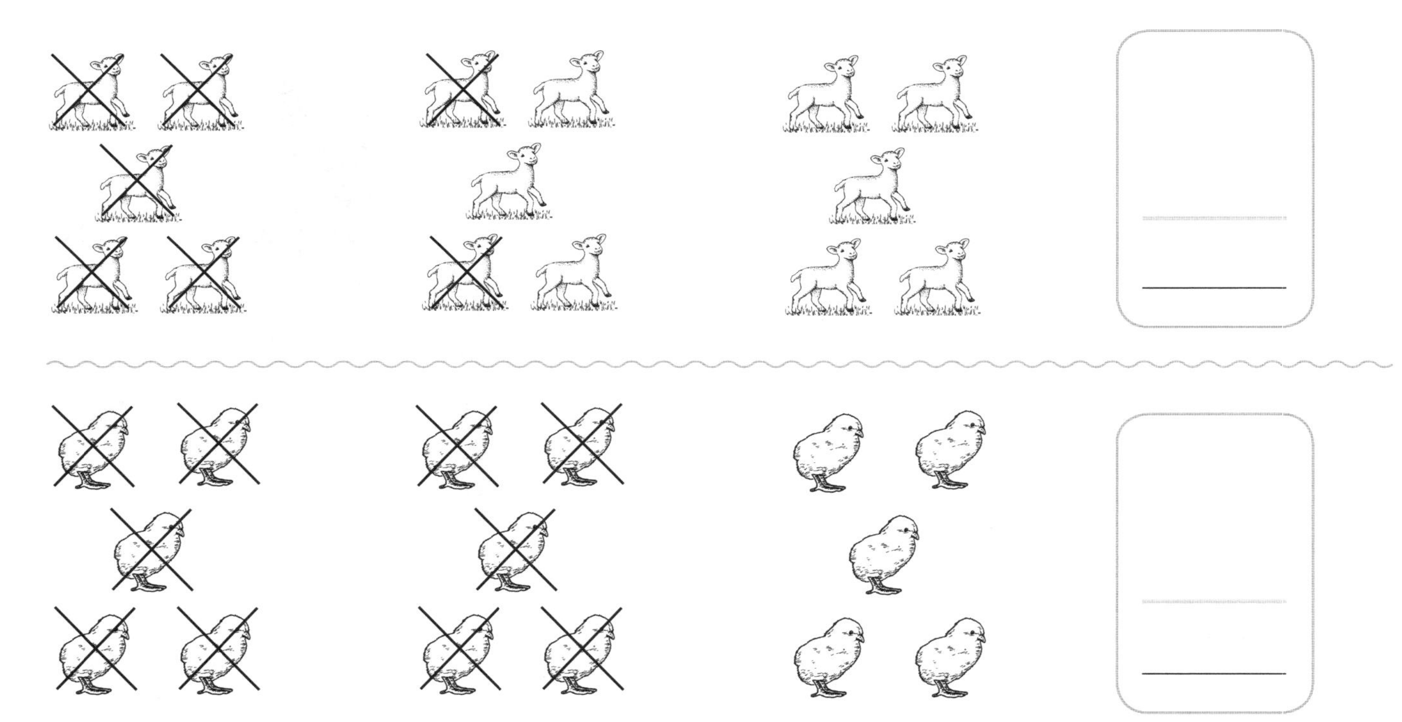

Fill in the missing whole or part. Be careful!

15	14	15	15	14	14	15	15
-	-	- 7	-	-	- 6	-	- 5
9	7		5	9		7	

Answer these subtraction facts.

10	12	10	15	9	14	11	13
- 5	- 3	- 6	- 6	- 4	- 5	- 3	- 7

9	12	14	11	13	15	10	15
- 2	- 6	- 6	- 5	- 6	-10	- 4	- 6

14	9	15	10	14	15	13	12
- 8	- 3	-10	- 3	- 7	- 9	- 5	- 4

12	15	12	11
- 7	- 8	- 5	- 2

If it's 1 child on a swing
Or 15 bees on wing,
*"His eye seeth
every precious thing."*
If it's 300 busy ants,
Or 400 tiny plants,
*"His eye seeth
every precious thing."*

Answer these subtraction problems. Borrow when you need to.

43	85	70	99	65	31
- 4	- 7	-23	-38	- 7	- 6

75	91	76	92	94	79
-36	-33	-15	-45	-16	-54

138 Draw lines of the correct length. Start at the dot.

$5\frac{1}{2}$" •

2" •

$3\frac{1}{2}$" •

$1\frac{1}{2}$" •

4" •

Count the money. Write the amount.

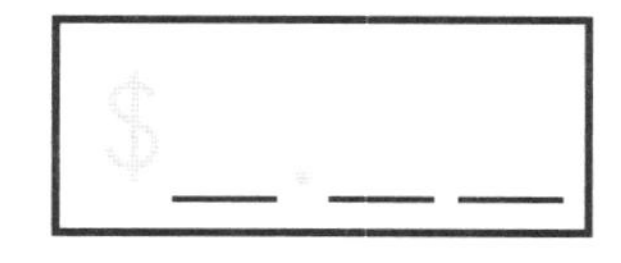

Trace and finish the rule.

______ ________________ = 1 gallon

Speed Drill

"Let us run
with patience the race
that is set before us."
Hebrews 12:1

13	15	12	14	14	11
- 4	- 8	- 5	- 8	- 5	- 6

13	11	15	11	12	14
- 7	- 7	- 6	- 5	- 3	- 9

11	14	12	15	11	13	15	13
- 4	- 6	- 7	- 6	- 3	- 8	- 7	- 6

13	12	15	11	13	12	14	15
- 9	- 6	- 9	- 2	- 5	- 4	- 7	- 7

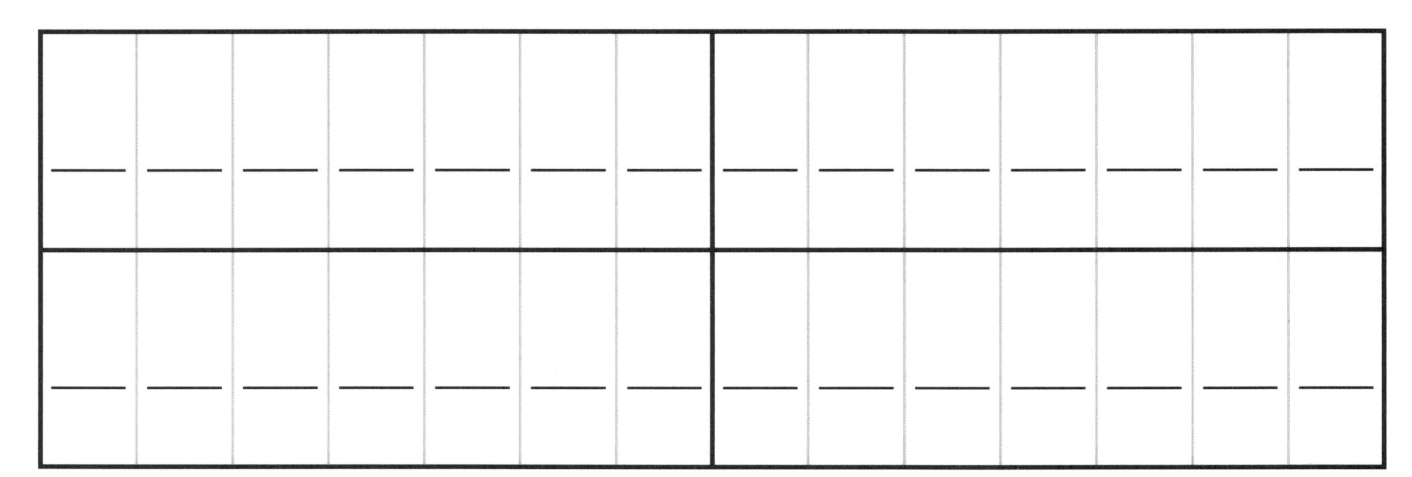

Fill in the whole and the parts.

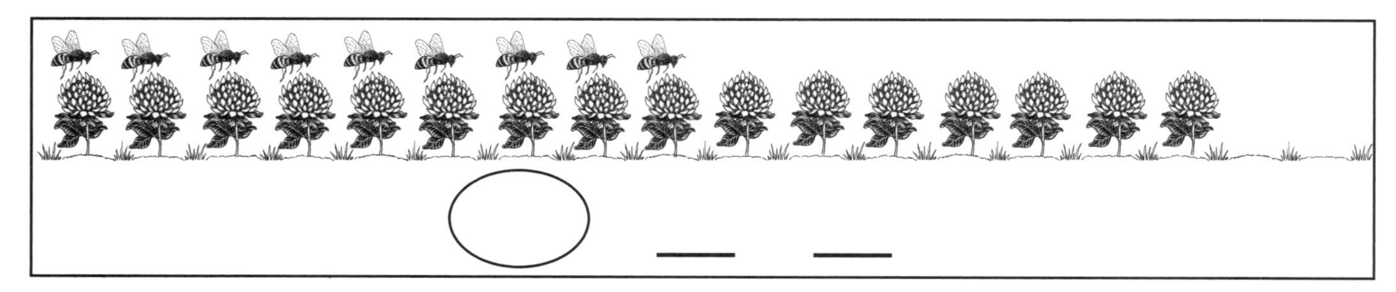

Write a fact for each picture.

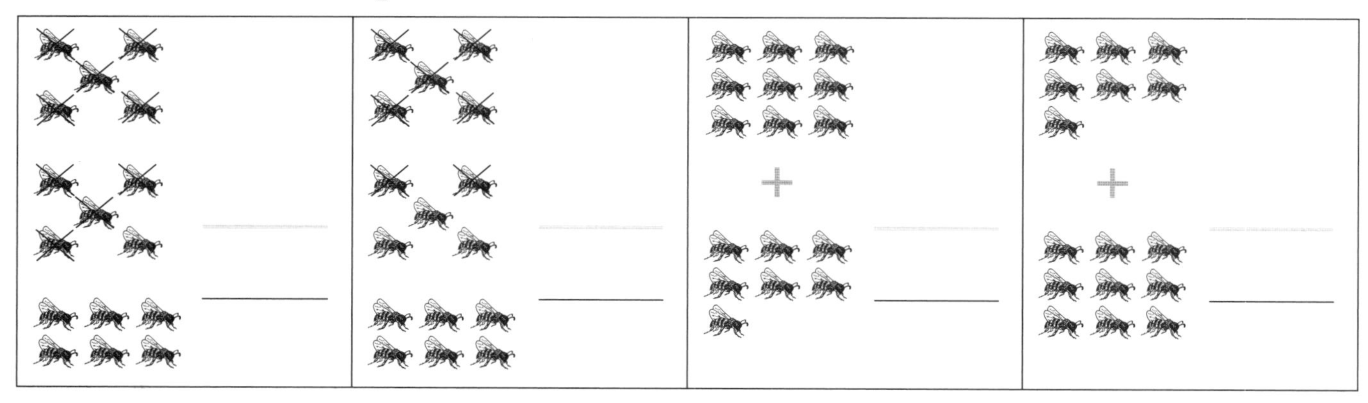

Trace and copy the triplet. Write the facts twice in the hives.

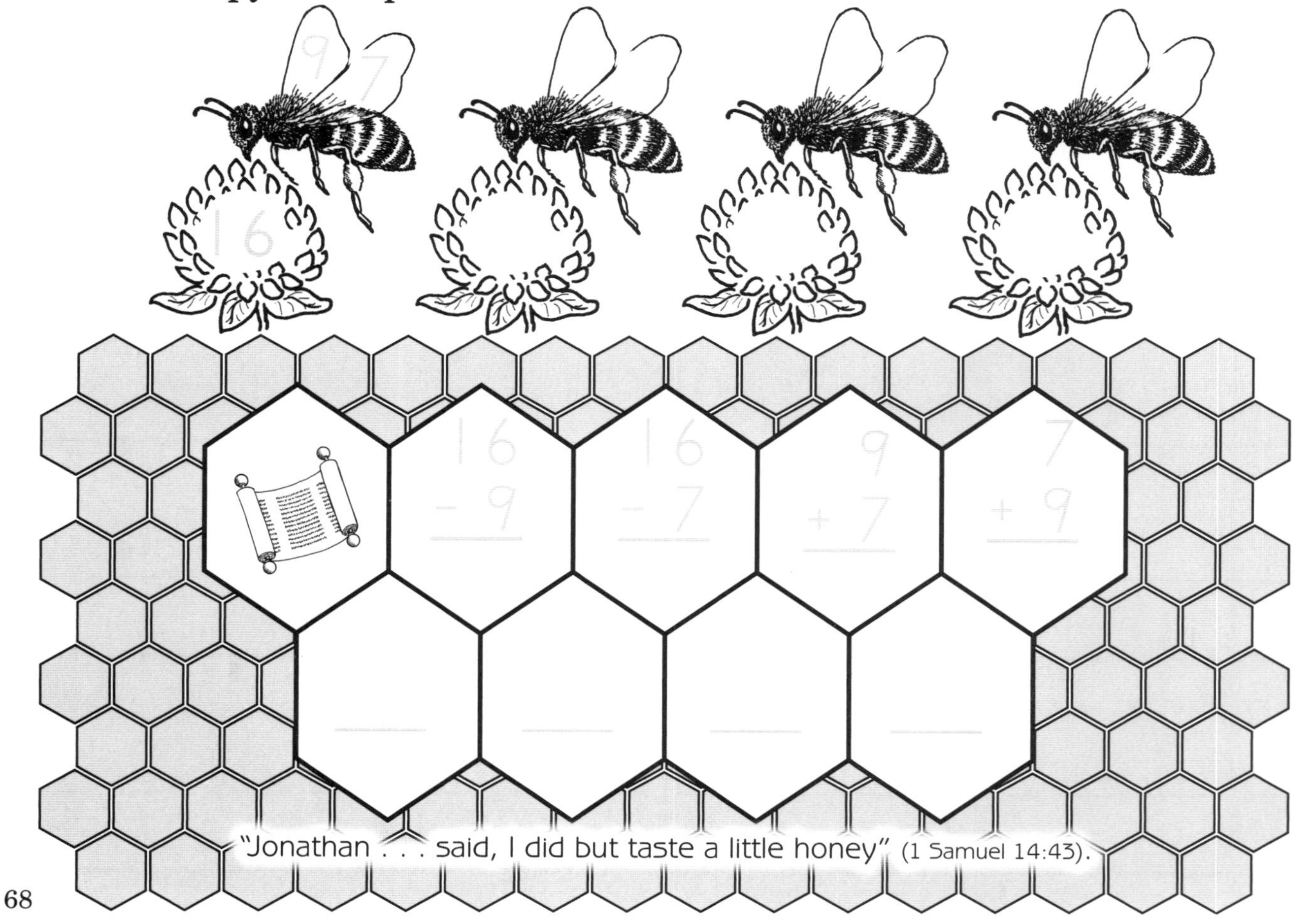

"Jonathan . . . said, I did but taste a little honey" (1 Samuel 14:43).

Answer these facts.

7	16	9	13	9	7	16	6
+ 9	− 9	+ 7	− 5	+ 7	+ 9	− 7	+ 8

7	16	8	16	14	7	16	9
+ 9	− 7	+ 5	− 9	− 8	+ 9	− 9	+ 7

16	8	7	13	14	7	16	9
− 7	+ 6	+ 9	− 8	− 6	+ 9	− 9	+ 7

16	7	5	9
− 7	+ 9	+ 8	+ 7

If it's 1 child on a swing
Or 16 bees on wing,
"His eye seeth
every precious thing."
If it's 500 hives at night,
Or 600 starbeams bright,
"His eye seeth
every precious thing."

Answer these problems. Carry when you need to.

169	64	156	167	82	86
− 72	+ 98	− 84	− 74	+ 66	+ 79

157	73	138	168	85	67
− 60	+ 75	− 45	− 96	+ 77	+ 98

139 Write the time.

Do these number strings.

15 − 6 − 4 + 2 + 6 = ___	3 + 1 + 7 − 2 − 5 = ___
14 − 9 + 3 + 4 − 7 = ___	11 − 6 + 1 + 3 + 6 = ___
2 + 5 + 8 − 6 − 2 = ___	7 + 6 − 5 + 2 − 4 = ___

Draw lines of the correct length. Start at the dot.

6" •

$5\frac{1}{2}$" •

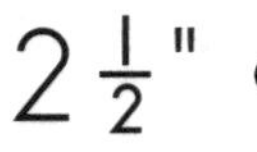

$2\frac{1}{2}$" •

God, make my life a little light,
Within the world to glow;
A little flame that burneth bright
Wherever I may go.
—Matilda B. B. Edwards

Answer these story problems.

Mother made one dozen pies. She took 8 pies to an all-day fellowship meeting. How many pies did she leave at home?

_____ ______________

_____ ______________

_____ ______________

Lois made 18 cookies to look like rabbits. Fay made 27 cookies to look like ducks. What is the sum of cookies the girls made?

_____ ______________

_____ ______________

_____ ______________

Trace and finish the rules.

_____ ______________ = 1 pint

2 pints = _____ ______________

4 quarts = _____ ______________

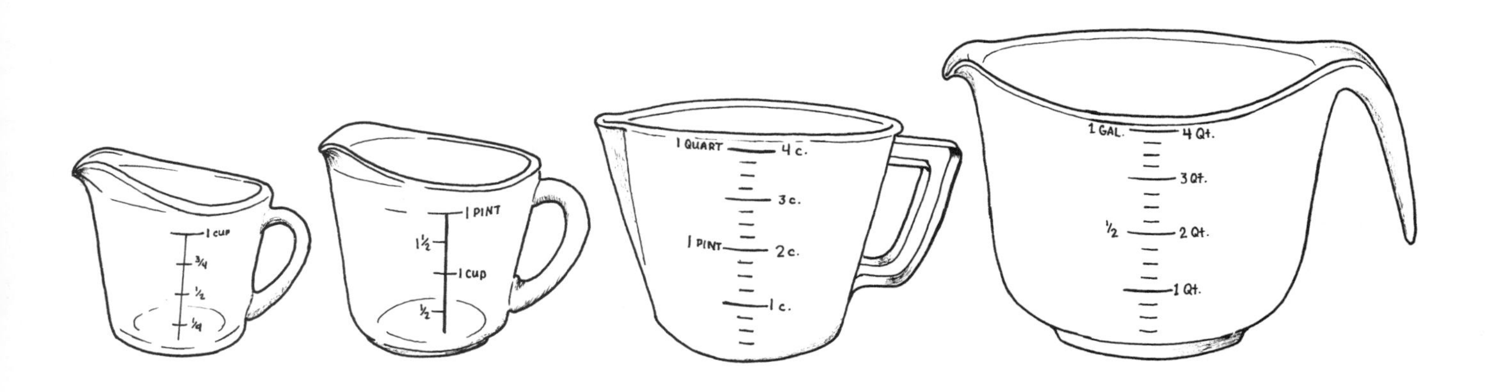

Fill in the whole and the parts.

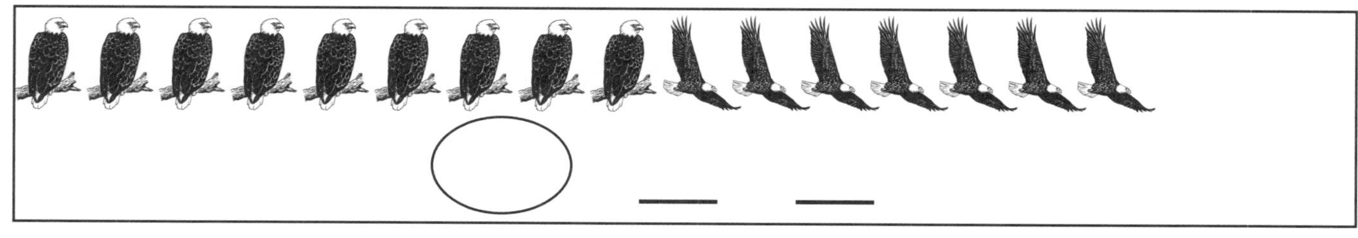

Answer the facts. Make the pictures fit the facts.
Your eagle can look like this one.

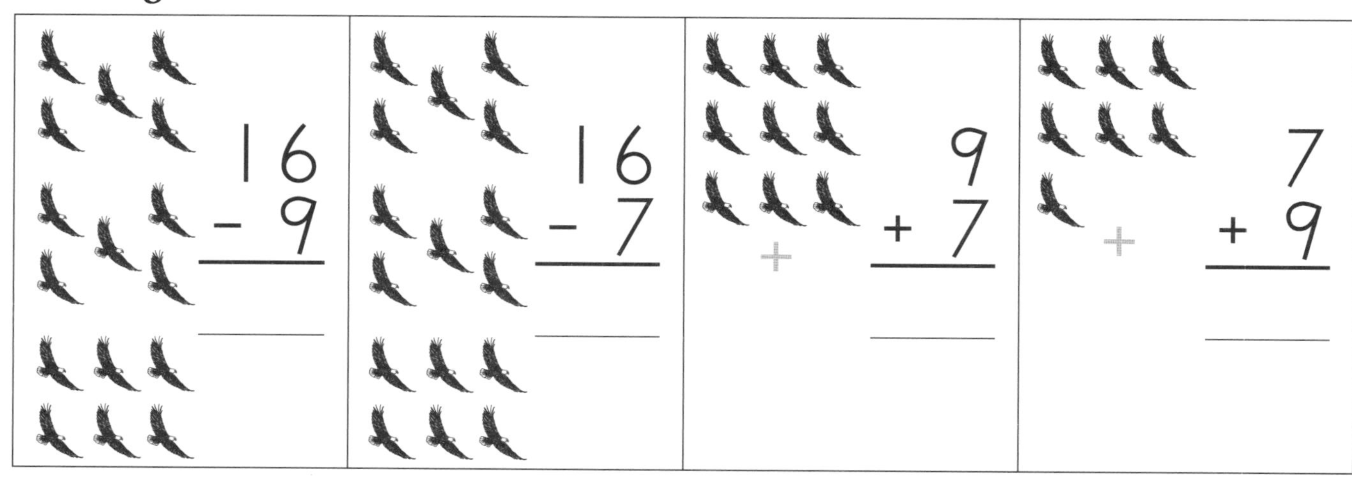

Trace and copy the triplet.

Write the four facts twice.

"And Jesus said unto him,
Foxes have holes, and birds
of the air have nests."

Luke 9:58

140

Answer these facts.

9	15	16	8	7	16	15	16
+ 7	− 9	− 7	+ 7	+ 9	− 7	− 9	− 9
16	7	9	16	7	15	16	9
− 7	+ 8	+ 7	− 9	+ 9	− 7	− 7	+ 6
7	16	15	9	15	16	15	7
+ 9	− 9	− 6	+ 7	− 7	− 7	− 6	+ 9

15	16	6	16
− 8	− 7	+ 9	− 9

If it's 1 child on a swing
Or 16 bees on wing,
*"His eye seeth
every precious thing."*
If it's 500 hives at night,
Or 600 starbeams bright,
*"His eye seeth
every precious thing."*

Answer these problems. Borrow when you need to.

96	99	95	99	77	96
−79	−76	−37	−67	−47	−57
65	84	57	95	66	55
−26	−26	−34	−65	−37	−38

140 Write the time.

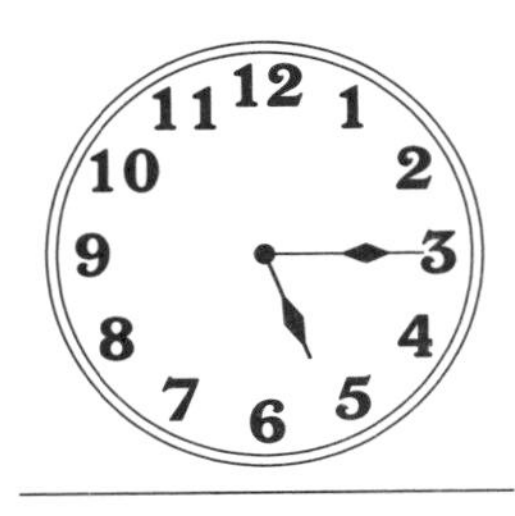

Count the money. Write the amount.

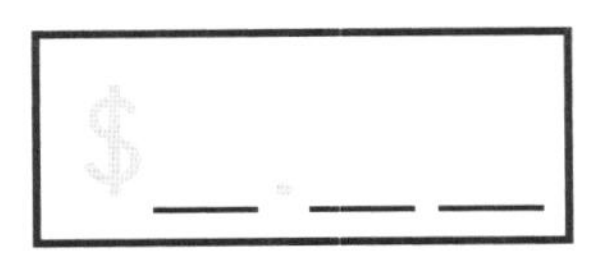

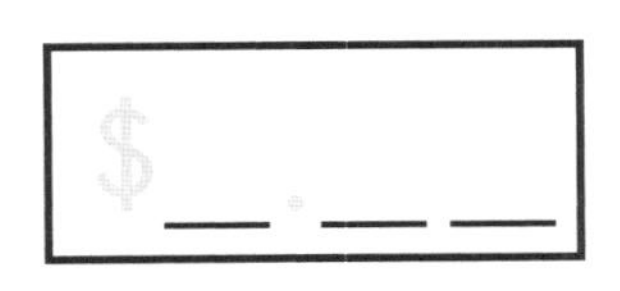

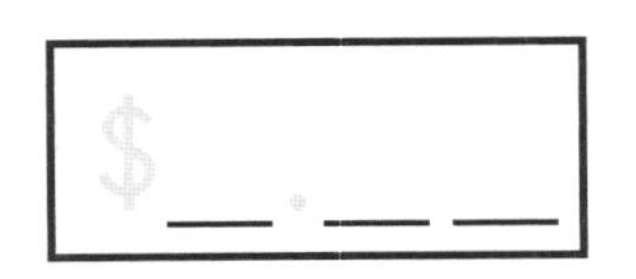

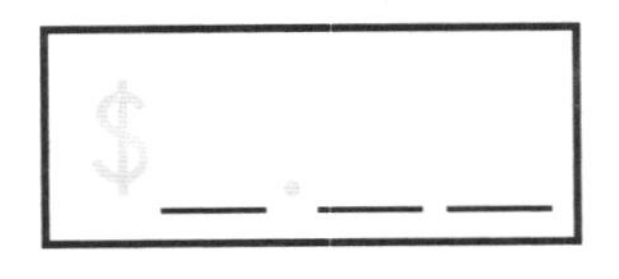

Speed Drill

"Giving all diligence . . ."
2 Peter 1:5

		$9 + 6$	$16 - 7$	$9 + 7$	$16 - 9$	$9 + 7$	$6 + 9$
		$16 - 9$	$9 + 6$	$7 + 9$	$15 - 6$	$9 + 7$	$16 - 7$
$15 - 9$	$16 - 7$	$7 + 9$	$6 + 9$	$9 + 7$	$7 + 9$	$16 - 9$	$15 - 6$
$9 + 7$	$15 - 9$	$9 + 6$	$16 - 9$	$16 - 7$	$16 - 9$	$15 - 6$	$7 + 9$

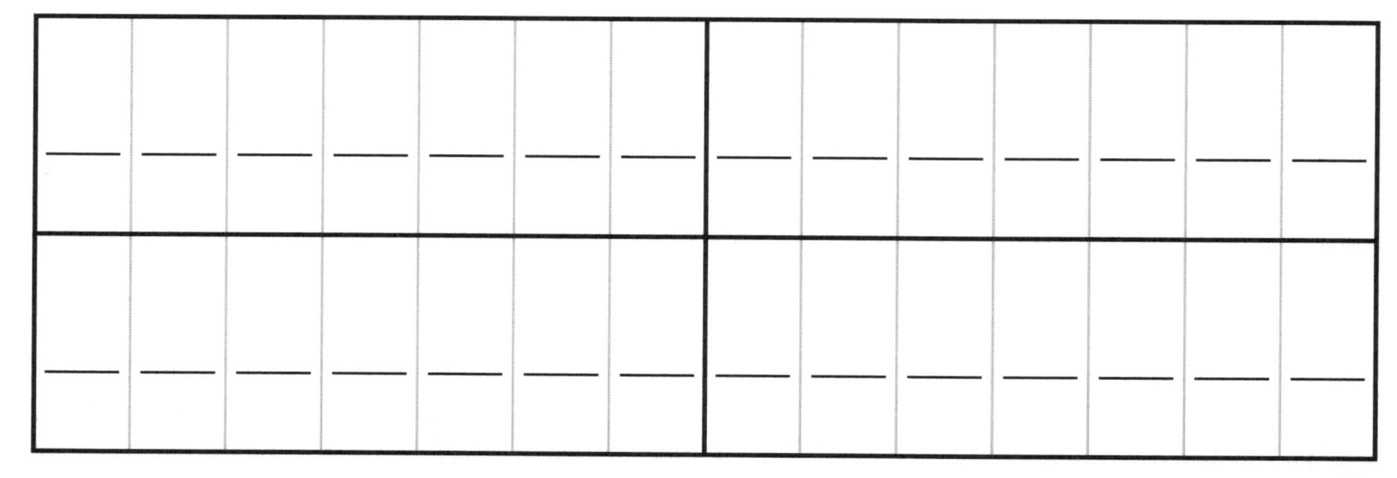

141 Fill in the whole and the parts. Write the facts.

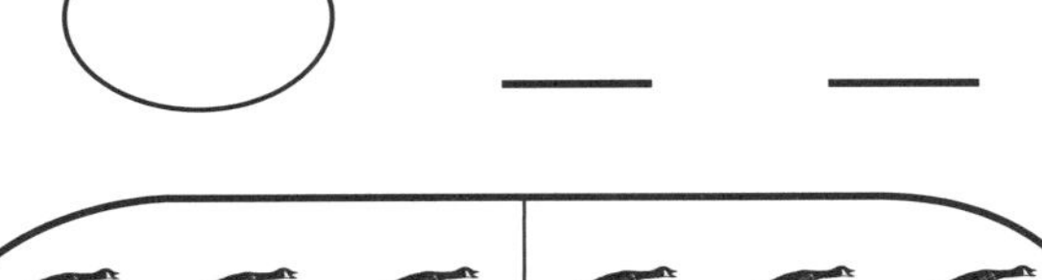

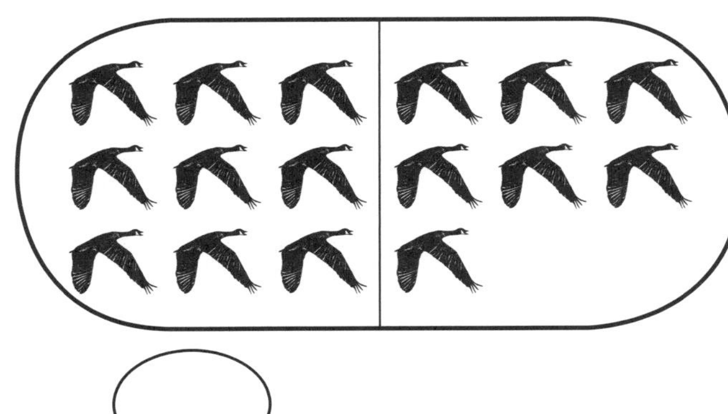

Fill in the missing whole or part.

16 − ___ = 9	9 + ___ = 16	___ − 9 = 7
15 − 8 = ___	8 + 7 = ___	7 + ___ = 16
___ + 7 = 16	16 − ___ = 7	___ − 7 = 8
15 − ___ = 7	___ + 8 = 15	7 + 9 = ___
7 + 9 = ___	15 − 7 = ___	7 + ___ = 15
___ − 7 = 9	___ + 9 = 16	___ − 7 = 9

Answer these addition problems. Carry when you need to. Remember the commas.

678 +467	328 +596	943 +727	486 +869	458 +184
663 +988	475 +779	246 +248	757 +488	857 +794
259 +383	579 +776	726 +944	266 +658	459 +686

Answer these story problems.

Last summer the Hersheys had 64 beehives. This week Father built six more hives. How many hives do they have for this summer?

Now their bee colony can gather about 25 pounds of nectar a day. If they gather 24 pounds one day and 27 pounds the next day, how much do they gather on those 2 days?

141

Write a fraction for the shaded part of each shape.
Circle the shapes that show fractions the same as $\frac{1}{2}$.

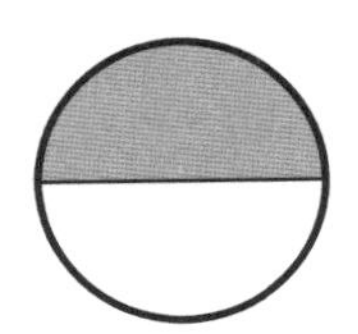 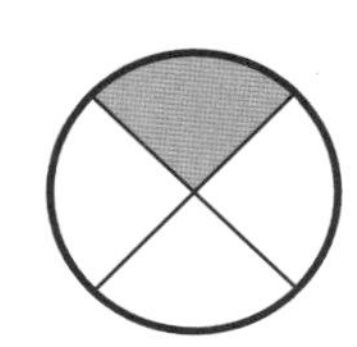 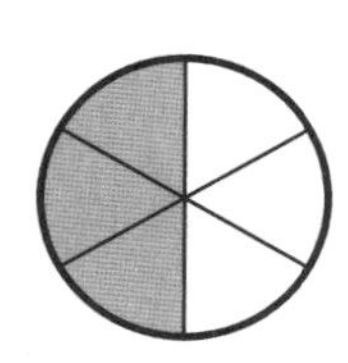 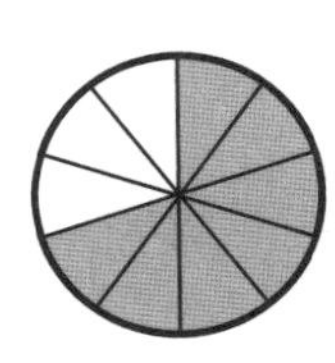 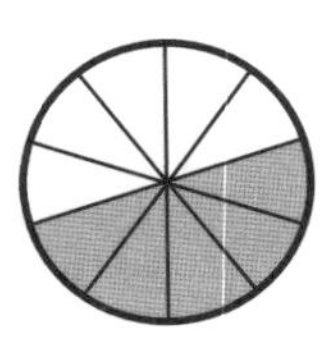

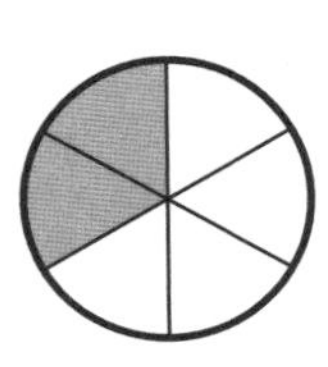 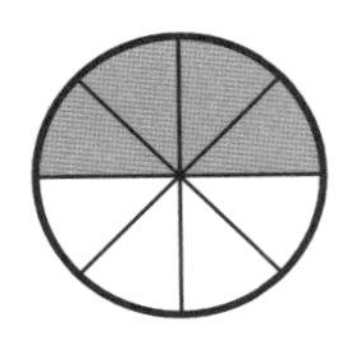 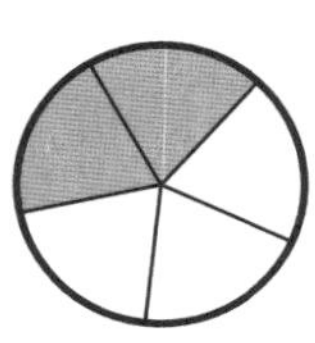 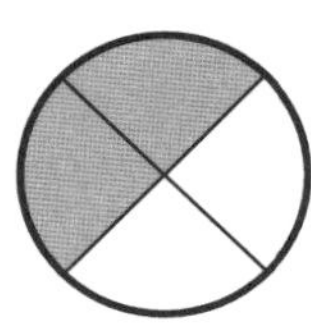 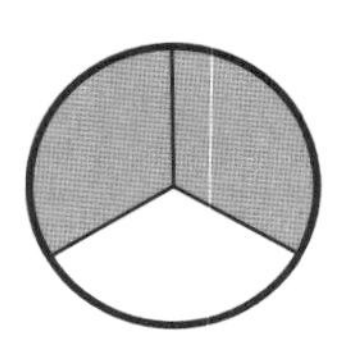

Trace and finish the rule. Then answer the questions.

Susan said, "It is one week until my birthday!"
How many days is that? ______________

Grandmother stayed with us for 1 week and 2 days.
How many days was she with us?
(Think: 1 week = 7 days.
7 days + 2 more days = ________ days.)

Count the money. Add the amounts.

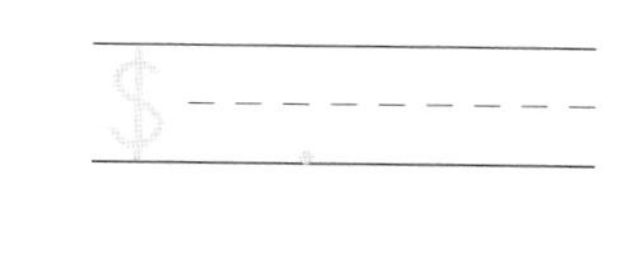

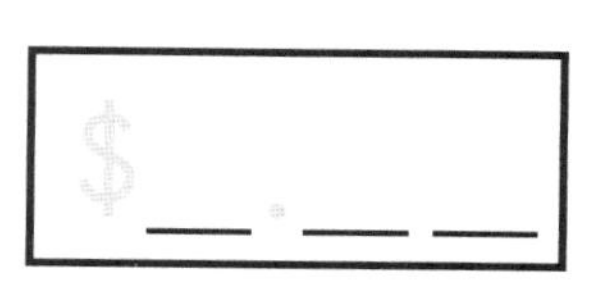

Measure these knives. Trace and finish the rules.

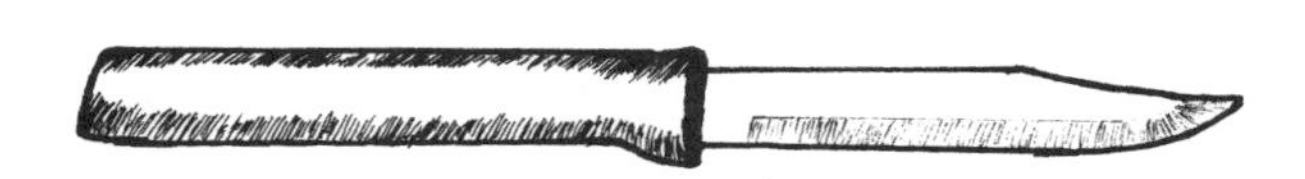

12 inches = ______ ______________

______ ______________ = 1 yard

142 Fill in the whole and the parts. Write the facts.

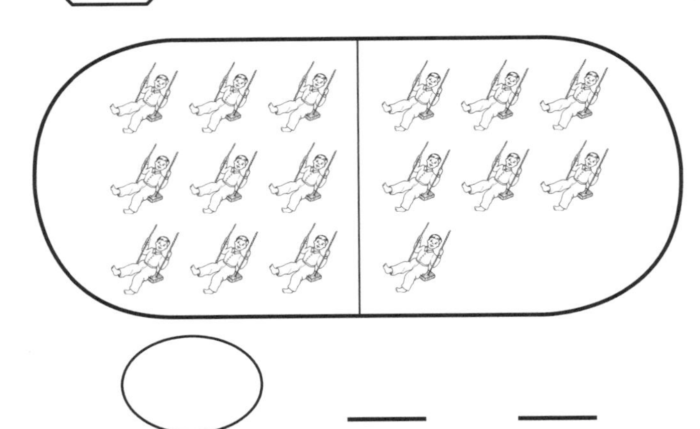

Answer these facts.

16 − 7	5 + 9	13 − 8	9 + 7	13 − 4	7 + 8	16 − 9	6 + 8
13 − 6	7 + 9	8 + 7	14 − 6	6 + 9	9 + 7	14 − 7	16 − 7
7 + 6	14 − 5	16 − 9	8 + 5	7 + 9	15 − 6	8 + 6	15 − 8
4 + 9	7 + 7	16 − 7	15 − 7	9 + 6	14 − 8	9 + 7	13 − 7

Answer these subtraction problems. Do not borrow.

852	1,463	1,087	974	1,667
- 630	- 623	- 526	- 321	-741

1,557	1,375	1,684	946	1,279
- 810	- 843	- 910	- 423	- 532

1,649	1,387	966	1,586	1,084
- 723	- 734	- 405	-746	- 862

Answer these story problems.

Lee had 37¢ in his bank. Today he earned 58¢ by shelling peas. How many cents does Lee have now?

24 children are playing tag. Eight children are on base. How many children are not on base?

142 Write the time.

Write the correct numbers.

1,542 has ____ hundreds.

186 has ____ ones.

3,471 has ____ thousands.

5,836 has ____ tens.

2,034 has ____ hundreds.

6,049 has ____ thousands.

1,908 has ____ hundreds.

502 has ____ tens.

4,360 has ____ ones.

8,818 has ____ ten.

Do these number strings.

16 − 9 + 1 + 3 − 5 = ____

3 + 4 + 3 − 2 + 4 = ____

13 − 4 − 3 + 8 − 5 = ____

11 − 9 + 3 + 1 + 4 = ____

Speed Drill

"Giving all diligence . . ."
2 Peter 1:5

15	7	16	15	6	9
− 6	+ 9	− 7	− 7	+ 9	+ 7

16	15	7	8	9	15
− 9	− 9	+ 9	+ 7	+ 6	− 8

15	9	16	6	7	15	7	16
− 7	+ 7	− 7	+ 9	+ 9	− 6	+ 8	− 9

7	9	16	7	15	9	16	15
+ 9	+ 6	− 7	+ 8	− 8	+ 7	− 9	− 9

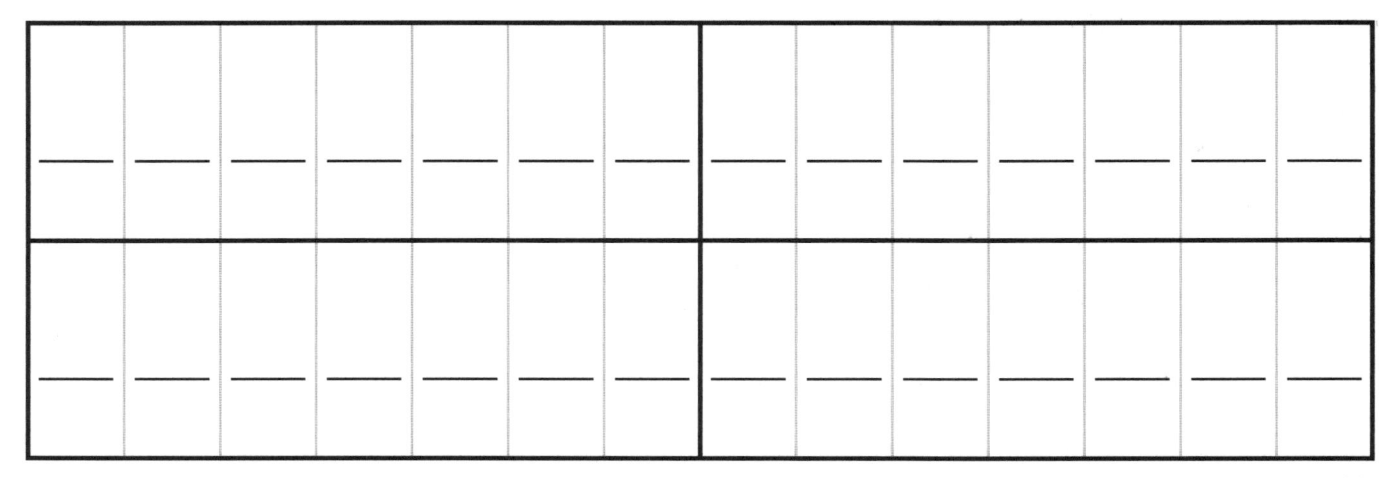

143

Write a fact and a triplet for each picture.

 + 

 + 

Answer these facts.

6	7	13	16	5	12	13	9
+ 9	+ 7	− 5	− 9	+ 9	− 4	− 6	+ 7

5	8	7	12	6	14	4	16
+ 7	+ 7	+ 9	− 5	+ 7	− 5	+ 9	− 7

14	6	16	13	5	14	7	12
− 7	+ 6	− 7	− 4	+ 8	− 6	+ 9	− 3

Answer these problems. Carry or borrow in every problem.

66 - 59	57 + 88	86 - 57	92 - 18	66 + 79	65 - 28
89 + 67	66 - 47	67 + 99	76 + 79	95 - 76	57 + 99
93 - 56	86 - 29	55 + 19	96 - 67	94 - 37	76 - 69

Answer these story problems.

A skunk scratched on a hive. 32 bees came out. The skunk ate 13 of them. How many bees flew away?

_____ _______________

_____ _______________

_____ _______________

This week Mother sold 14 gallons of honey. Crystal sold 9 gallons. How many gallons of honey did they sell?

_____ _______________

_____ _______________

_____ _______________

If it's 1 child on a swing or 16 bees on wing,
"His eye seeth every precious thing."
If it's 500 hives at night, or 600 starbeams bright,
"His eye seeth every precious thing."

143 Write the digits in the correct places.

	ten thousands	thousands	hundreds	tens	ones
1,625					
17,493					
758					
6					
25,840					

Write a fraction for the shaded part of each shape.
Circle the shapes that show fractions the same as $\frac{1}{2}$.

Use the calendar page to answer the questions.

August						
Sunday	Monday	Tuesday	Wednesday	Thursday	Friday	Saturday
					1	2
3	4	5	6	7	8	9
10	11	12	13	14	15	16
17	18	19	20	21	22	23
24	25	26	27	28	29	30
31						

1. Name the days of the week.

_______________, _______________, _______________,

_______________, _______________,

_______________, _______________

2. Write the name of the first month of the year. _______________

3. Write the name of the last month of the year. _______________

4. The calendar page above shows the month of _______________.

5. August ends on a Sunday, so
   September will start on a _______________.

6. August 13 is a _______________.

7. August has __________ days.

144

Write a fact and a triplet for each picture.

Answer these facts.

7 + 9	9 + 6	12 − 6	9 + 4	8 + 6	16 − 7	12 − 9	8 + 7
12 − 7	14 − 9	8 + 5	16 − 9	9 + 7	12 − 8	7 + 7	7 + 5
6 + 6	13 − 8	7 + 9	14 − 8	7 + 6	16 − 7	13 − 9	8 + 4

Answer these subtraction problems. Borrow once in each problem.

144

696	975	839	947	866
-237	-757	-484	-381	-227
690	685	929	764	974
-118	-538	-257	-192	-827
891	786	829	717	975
-673	-327	-263	-362	-336

Write the time.

God, make my life a little song
That comforteth the sad;
That helpeth others to be strong,
And makes the singer glad.

—Matilda B. B. Edwards

144

Answer these story problems.

Father pays 67¢ for a small bolt and 99¢ for a large bolt. How many cents does he pay for both bolts?

Father has one dozen stamps in his desk. He sticks 5 of them on envelopes. How many stamps are left in his desk?

Write the digits in the correct places.

	ten thousands	thousands	hundreds	tens	ones
981					
1,502					
65					
73,413					
5,079					
38,140					
90,158					

Speed Drill

14	16	15	15	14	16
- 8	- 7	- 9	- 7	- 5	- 9

14	16	15	16	15	14
- 6	- 7	- 8	- 9	- 6	- 5

"Giving all diligence . . ."
2 Peter 1:5

14	16	16	15	15	14	16	14
- 7	- 9	- 7	- 9	- 7	- 7	- 7	- 9

4	4	8	2	8	4	7	6
1	2	1	6	1	4	2	2
+ 9	+ 7	+ 4	+ 7	+ 6	+ 5	+ 6	+ 7

145 Write all the triplets that you have learned.

11	12	13
◯ ___ ___	◯ ___ ___	◯ ___ ___
◯ ___ ___	◯ ___ ___	◯ ___ ___
◯ ___ ___	◯ ___ ___	◯ ___ ___
◯ ___ ___	◯ ___ ___	
14	**15**	**16**
◯ ___ ___	◯ ___ ___	◯ ___ ___
◯ ___ ___	◯ ___ ___	
◯ ___ ___		

Answer these facts.

15	5	16	7	4	14	10	7
− 6	+ 7	− 7	+ 6	+ 5	− 7	− 1	+ 9
___	___	___	___	___	___	___	___

2	7	11	6	10	9	3	12
+ 8	+ 7	− 4	+ 9	− 2	+ 7	+ 6	− 3
___	___	___	___	___	___	___	___

9	13	10	13	2	5	5	12
− 4	− 4	− 6	− 5	+ 7	+ 5	+ 9	− 4
___	___	___	___	___	___	___	___

2	10	11	4	9	16	4	10
+ 9	− 7	− 5	+ 9	− 3	− 9	+ 8	− 5
___	___	___	___	___	___	___	___

5	7	12	5	13	11
+ 8	+ 9	− 5	+ 6	− 6	− 3
___	___	___	___	___	___

Answer these problems.

55	57	64	81	35	32
23	42	73	75	63	45
+ 4	+ 6	+ 9	+ 8	+ 7	+ 5
___	___	___	___	___	___

74	54	56	45	24	45
15	33	12	33	44	32
+67	+78	+66	+65	+97	+79
___	___	___	___	___	___

If it's 1 child on a swing, / Or 16 bees on wing, / *"His eye seeth every precious thing."*
If it's 500 hives at night, / Or 600 starbeams bright, / *"His eye seeth every precious thing."*

145 This is a bar graph.

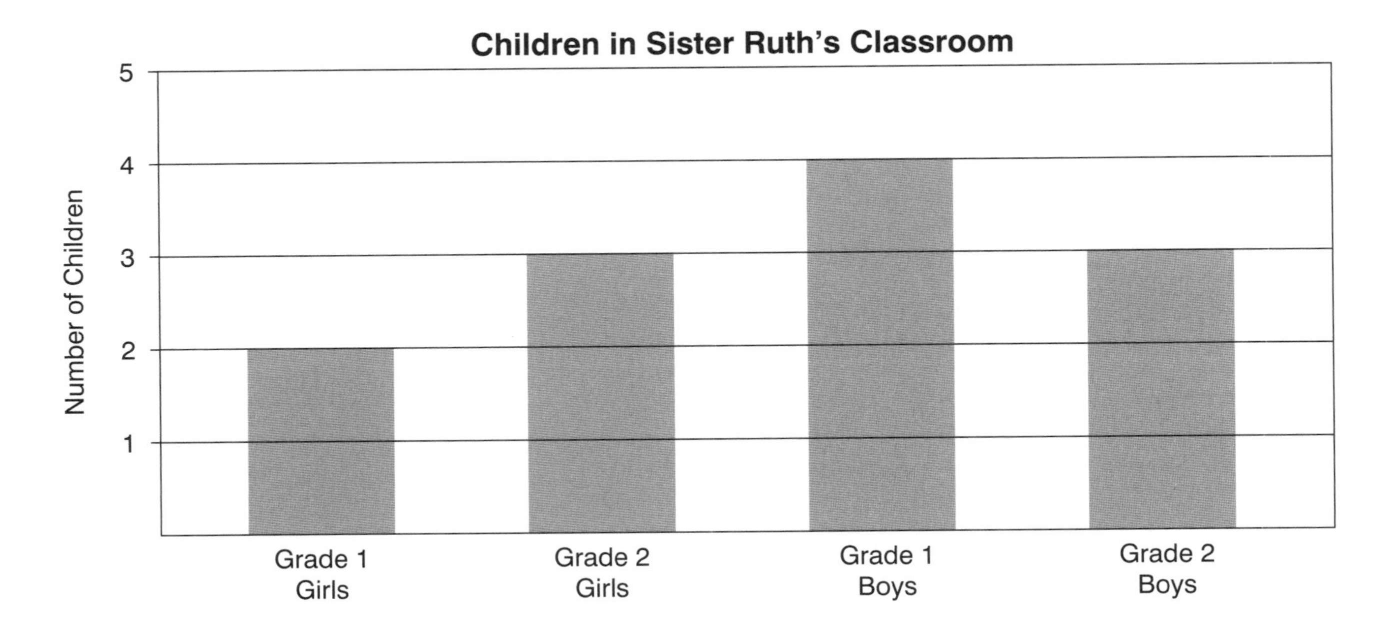

Study the bar graph and answer the questions.

1. How many boys are in Grade 1? ____________
2. How many girls are in Grade 1? ____________
3. How many students are in Grade 1? ____________
4. How many boys are in the whole classroom? ____________
5. How many children altogether are in Sister Ruth's room? ____________

Do these number strings.

$4 + 8 - 6 + 2 + 7 =$ ___

$16 - 7 + 2 - 5 + 8 =$ ___

$2 + 2 + 3 + 6 - 5 =$ ___

$5 - 2 + 4 + 4 - 8 =$ ___

$9 + 6 - 8 + 2 - 8 =$ ___

$16 - 9 - 3 - 2 + 7 =$ ___

Count the money. Add the amounts.

Write a fraction for the shaded part of each shape.
Circle the shapes that show fractions the same as 1 whole.

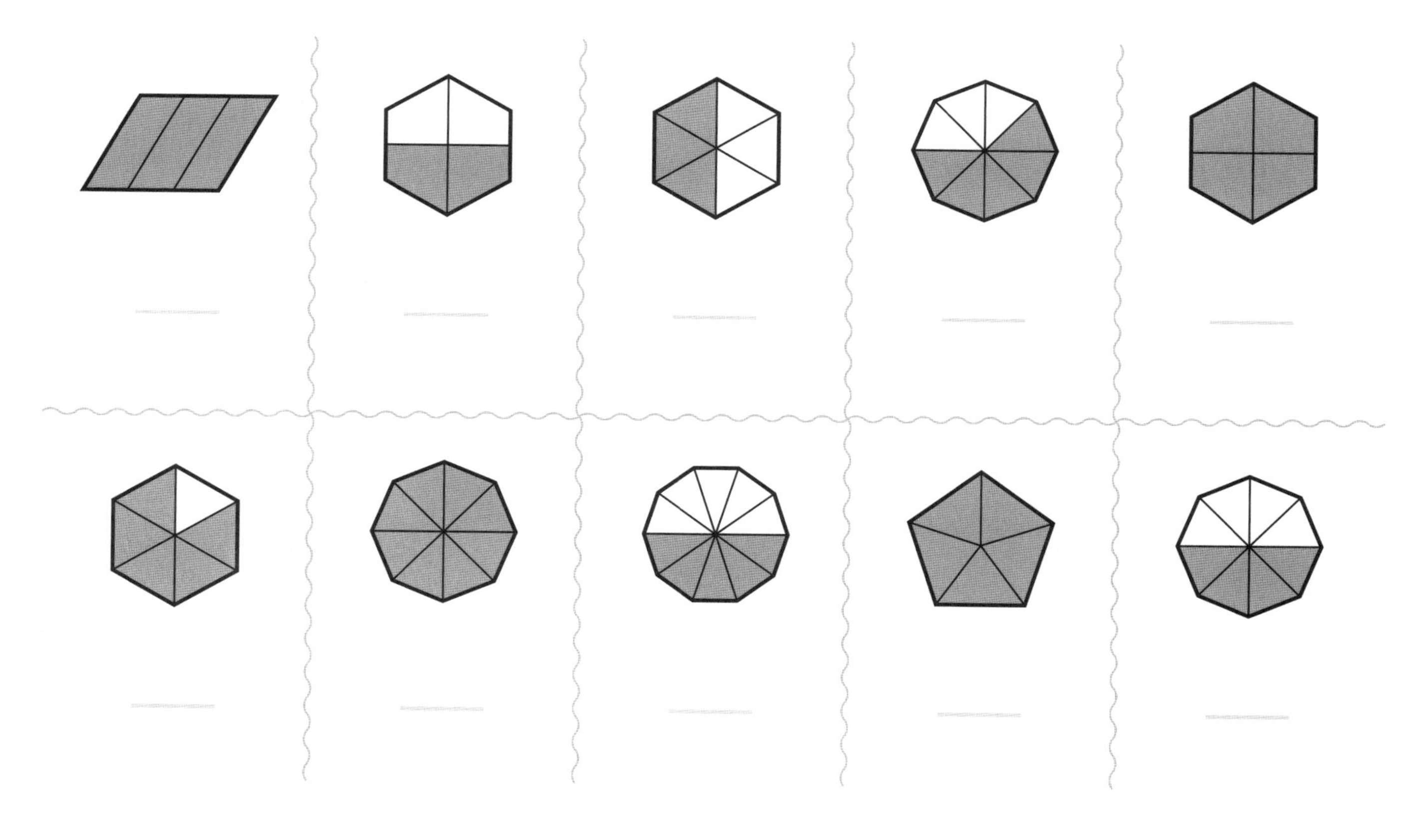

146 Fill in the whole and the parts.

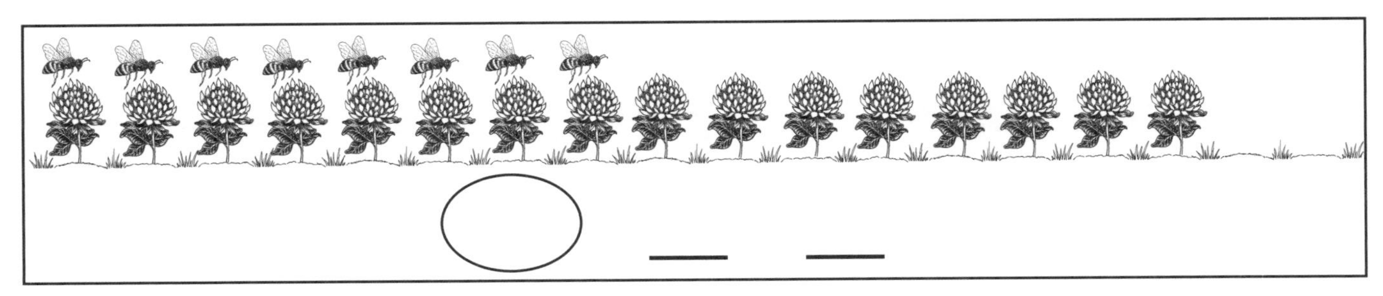

Write a fact for each picture.

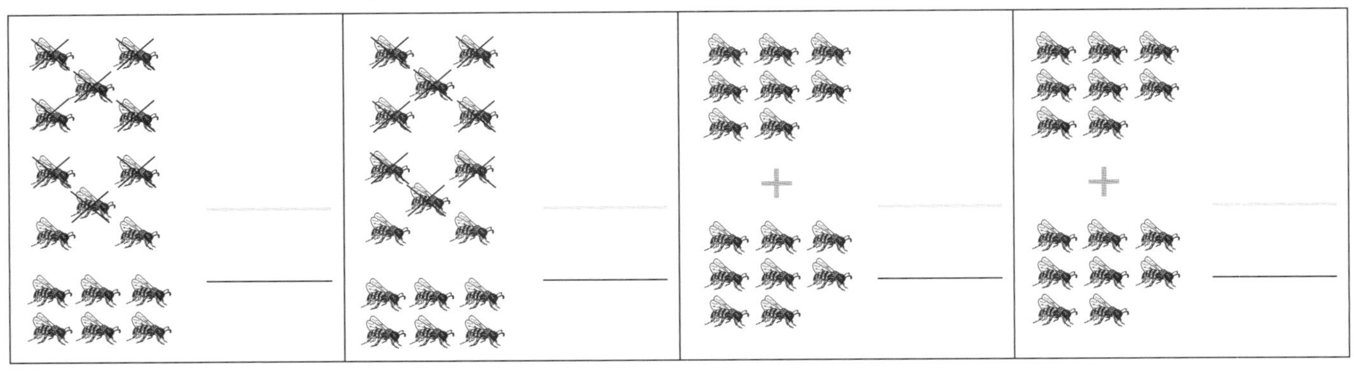

Trace and copy the triplet. Fill the honeycomb below with the facts.

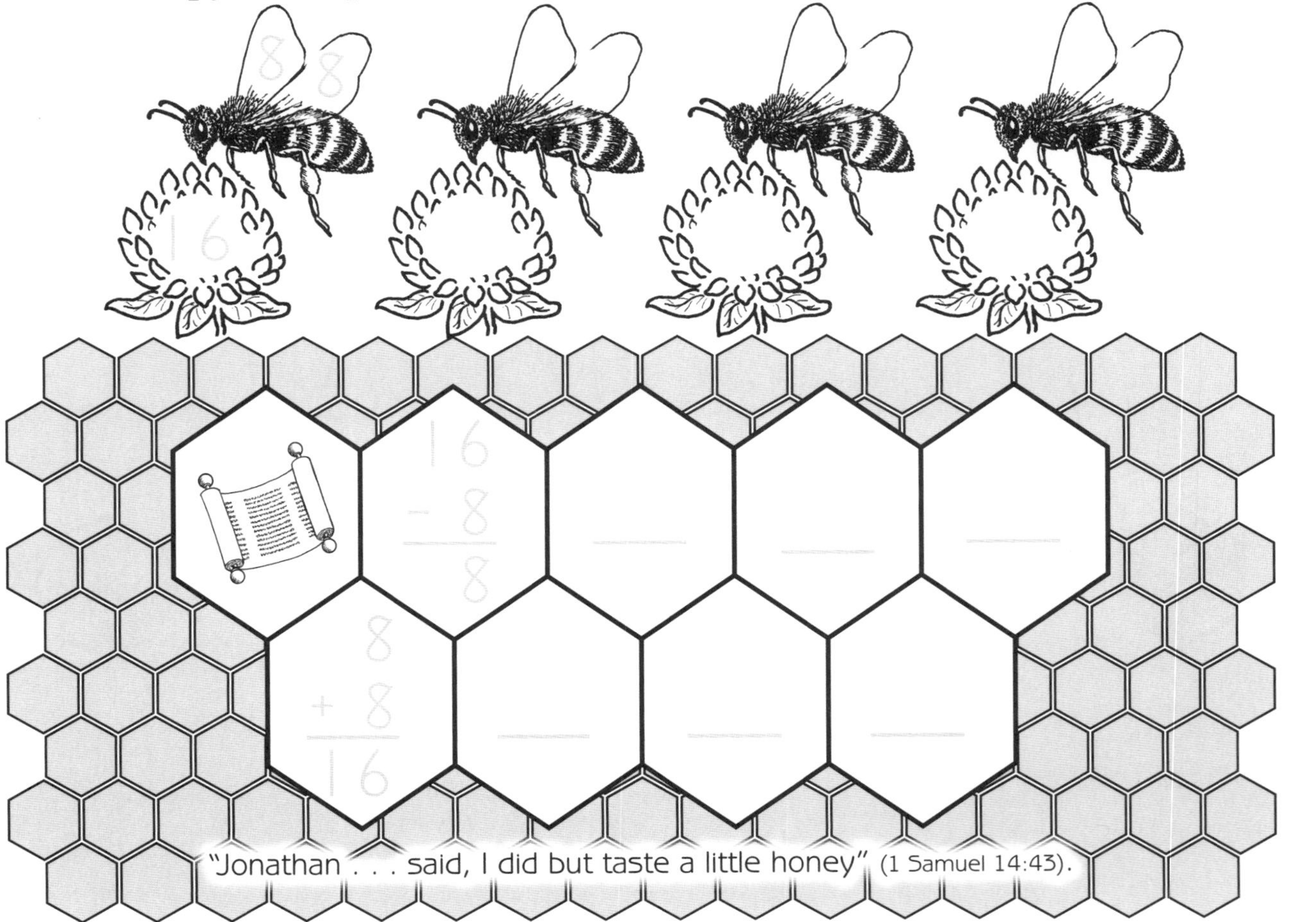

"Jonathan . . . said, I did but taste a little honey" (1 Samuel 14:43).

Answer these facts.

8 + 8	16 − 8	7 + 9	16 − 8	9 + 6	16 − 9	16 − 8	8 + 8
16 − 9	16 − 8	15 − 9	8 + 8	7 + 9	16 − 7	8 + 8	16 − 8
9 + 7	8 + 8	16 − 8	9 + 7	6 + 9	16 − 7	16 − 8	8 + 8

Answer these problems. Carry or borrow in every problem.

86 − 48	78 + 78	95 − 88	86 − 58	67 + 89	75 − 48
88 + 58	96 − 38	96 − 29	85 − 27	57 + 89	95 − 19
66 − 39	76 + 89	96 − 68	54 − 47	87 + 78	66 − 28

146 Count the money. Write the amount.

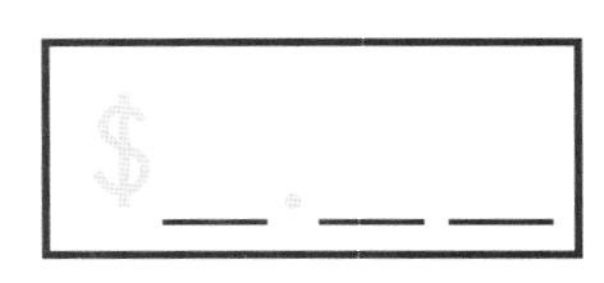

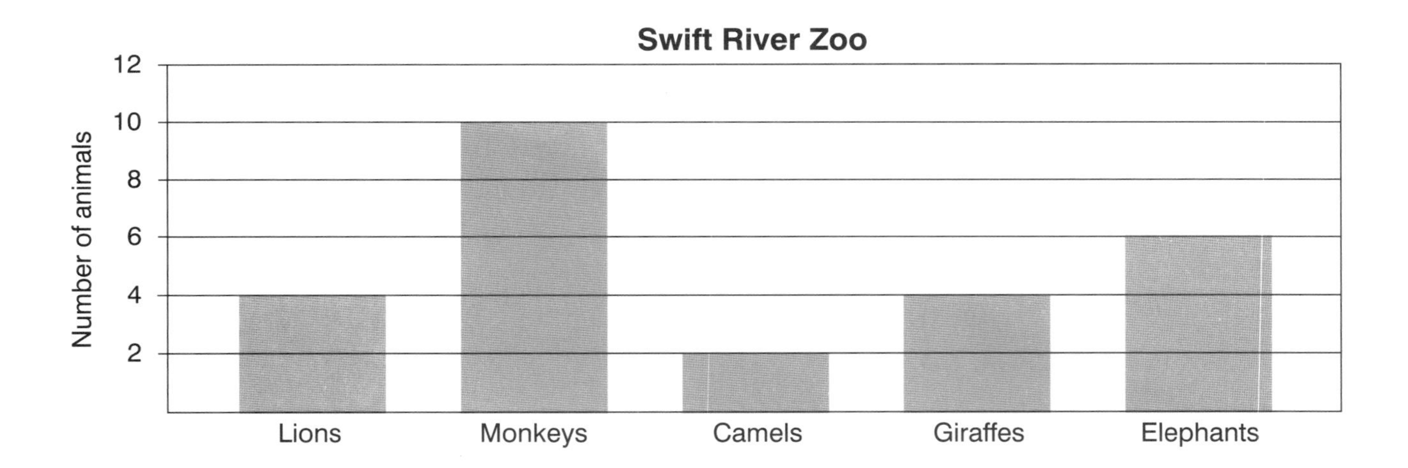

Study the bar graph and answer the questions.

1. There are the most ______________________ at the zoo.
2. There are the least ______________________ at the zoo.
3. There are the same number of ______________________ and ______________________.
4. How many more elephants than lions are there? __________

Speed Drill

"Giving all diligence . . ."
2 Peter 1:5

12	14	16	15	10	11
- 4	- 5	- 7	- 6	- 8	- 5

16	11	14	9	12	11
- 9	- 4	- 7	- 3	- 6	- 3

13	15	10	13	14	10	16	12
- 6	- 8	- 7	- 5	- 6	- 5	- 7	- 5

9	13	11	9	15	10	12	14
- 2	- 4	- 2	- 4	- 7	- 6	- 3	- 8

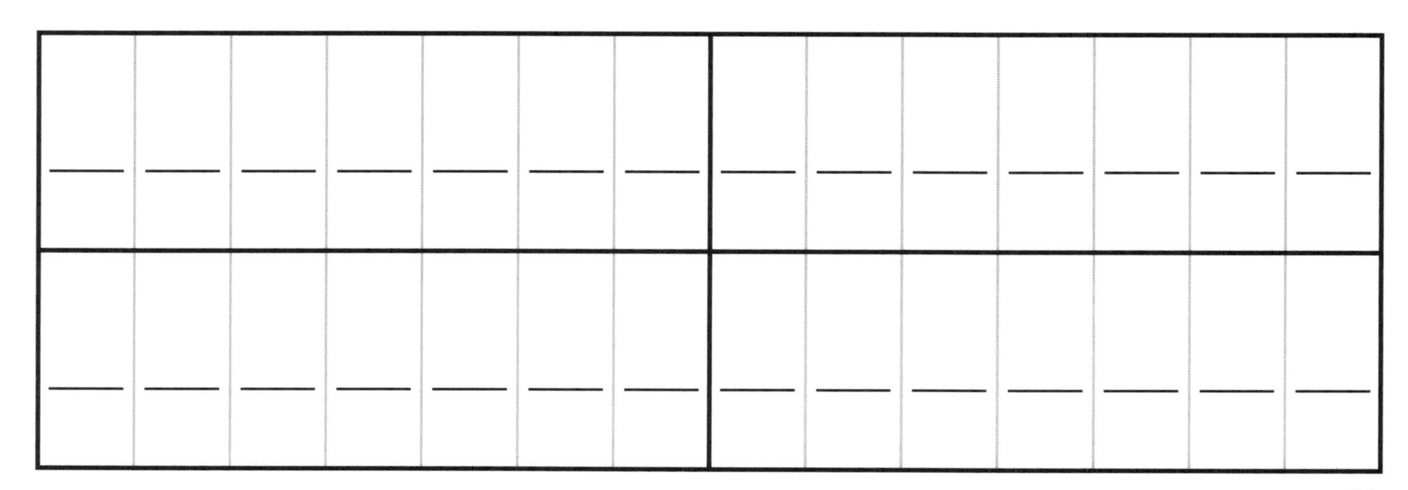

Fill in the whole and the parts.

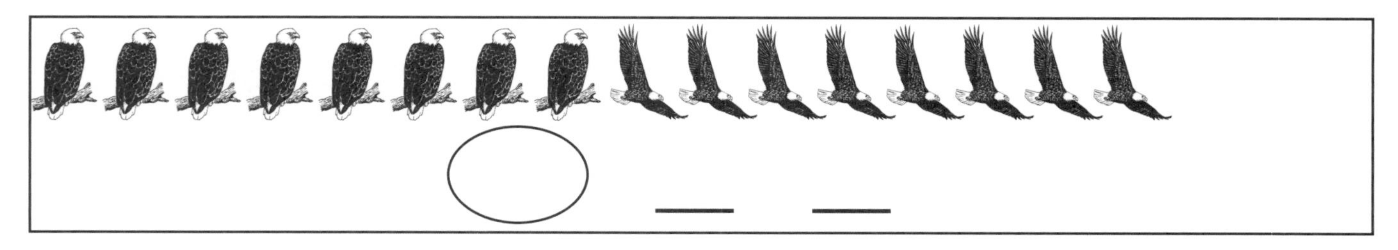

Answer the facts. Make the pictures fit the facts.

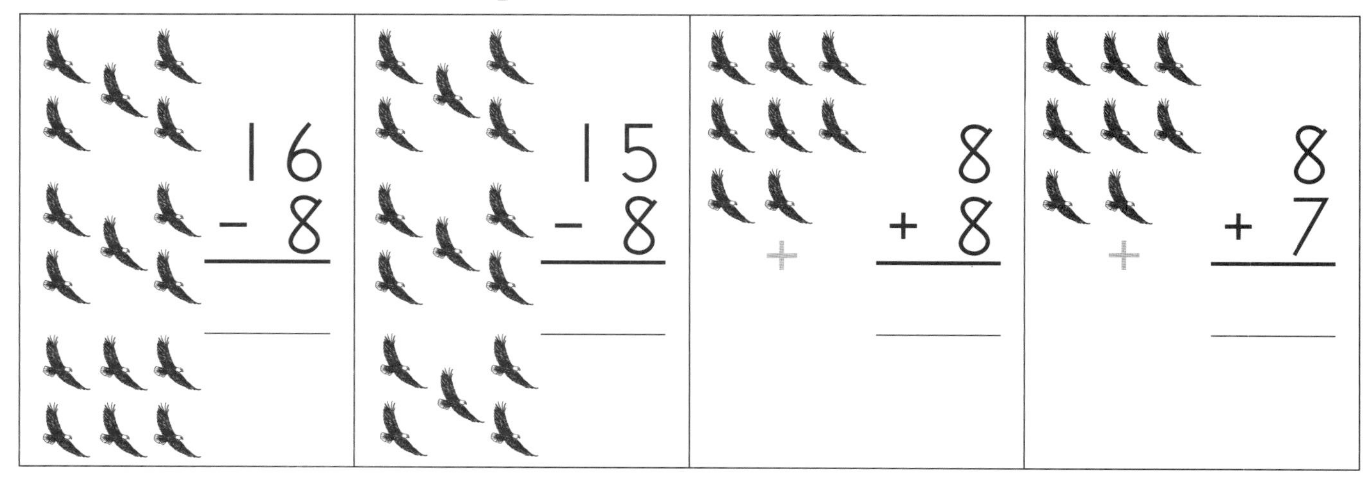

Trace and copy the triplet.

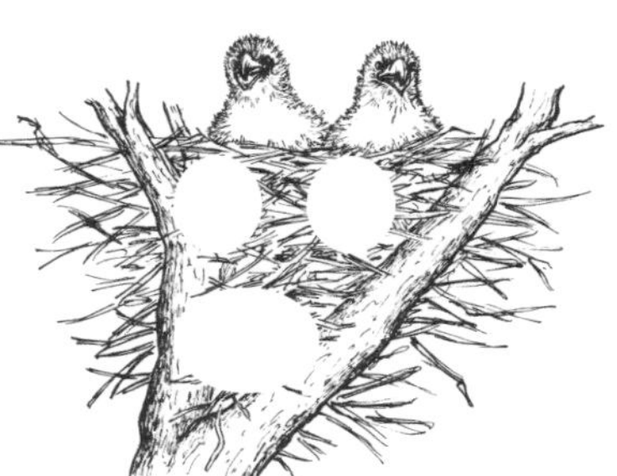

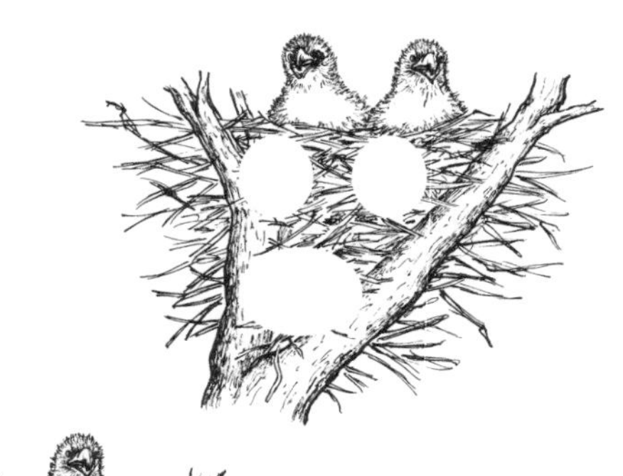

Write the two facts four times each.

"And Jesus said unto him, Foxes have holes, and birds of the air have nests."
Luke 9:58

Answer these facts.

16	15	16	8	15	7	16	6
− 8	− 7	− 9	+ 8	− 9	+ 8	− 8	+ 9

8	7	8	9	16	8	15	16
+ 6	+ 9	+ 8	+ 6	− 8	+ 8	− 8	− 7

7	16	8	14	8	9
+ 7	− 8	+ 7	− 8	+ 8	+ 7

If it's 1 child on a swing
Or 16 bees on wing,
"His eye seeth
every precious thing."
If it's 500 hives at night,
Or 600 starbeams bright,
"His eye seeth
every precious thing."

Answer these problems. Carry when you need to.

169	78	72	159	164
− 87	+ 87	+ 86	− 85	− 84

77	158	78	93	137	166
+ 59	− 76	+ 78	+ 65	− 90	− 86

158	88	167	77	83	158
− 94	+ 58	− 85	+ 88	+ 75	− 84

147 **Answer these story problems.**

Father has 75 tulips in his greenhouse and 85 tulips in his yard. How many tulips does Father have?

Twenty geese swim on the pond. *Honk, honk!* Soon four geese fly away. How many geese are still swimming?

Mohan's father harvested 56 kilograms of peanuts from his field. He sold 28 kilograms. How many kilograms of peanuts are left for his family?

Circle the digit in the thousands' place.

82,556	1,082	24,901
749	59,170	6,834
4,325	63,494	998

Answer these subtraction problems. Borrow once in each problem.

$$\begin{array}{r}895\\-267\\\hline\end{array}\quad\begin{array}{r}938\\-475\\\hline\end{array}\quad\begin{array}{r}880\\-112\\\hline\end{array}\quad\begin{array}{r}976\\-348\\\hline\end{array}\quad\begin{array}{r}645\\-182\\\hline\end{array}$$

Count the money. Add the amounts.

+ $

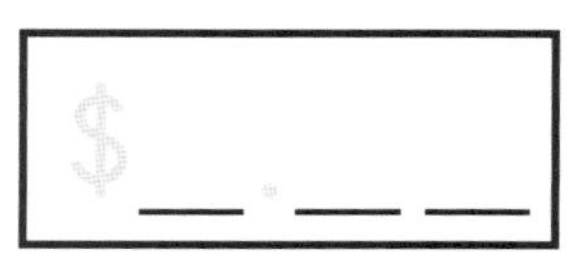

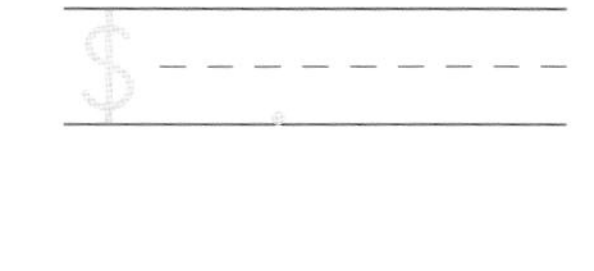

+ $

❖ Extra: Can you do these? ❖

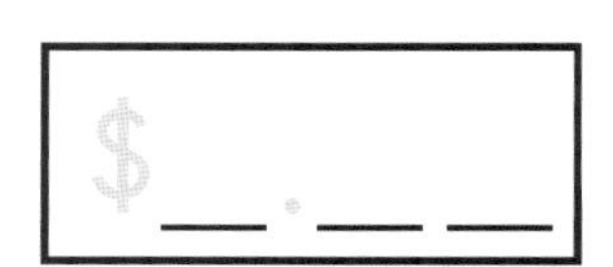

148

Write a fact and a triplet for each picture.

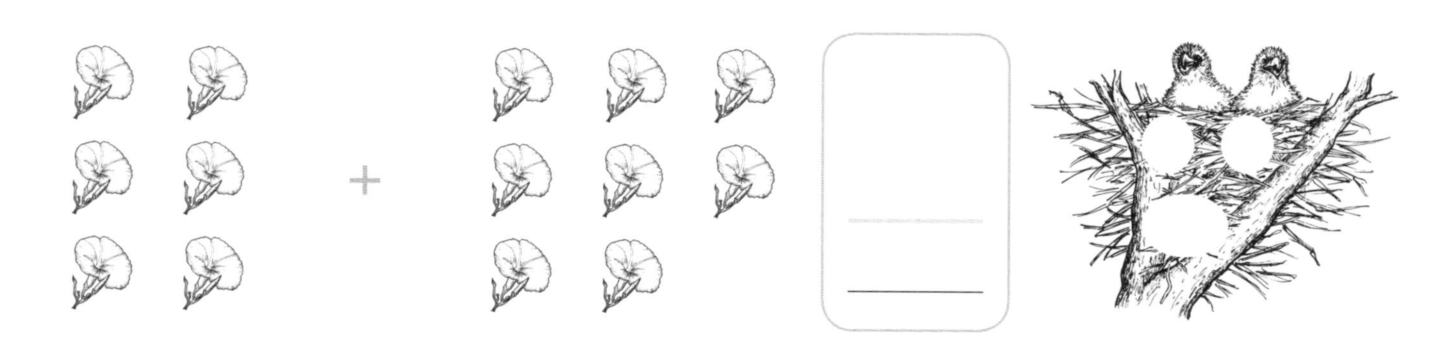

Answer these facts.

9	16	13	16	7	15	5	8
+ 6	− 9	− 4	− 8	+ 7	− 8	+ 8	+ 8
14	8	13	9	5	7	16	4
− 8	+ 8	− 7	+ 7	+ 9	+ 8	− 8	+ 9
14	7	13	16	14	8	6	15
− 6	+ 9	− 8	− 8	− 5	+ 8	+ 7	− 6

Answer these addition problems.
Carry one or two times in each problem.

239	837	266	664	771
+387	+268	+529	+683	+839
777	523	847	636	746
+857	+359	+557	+998	+136
678	468	855	359	855
+427	+158	+492	+436	+755

Study the bar graph, and answer the questions.

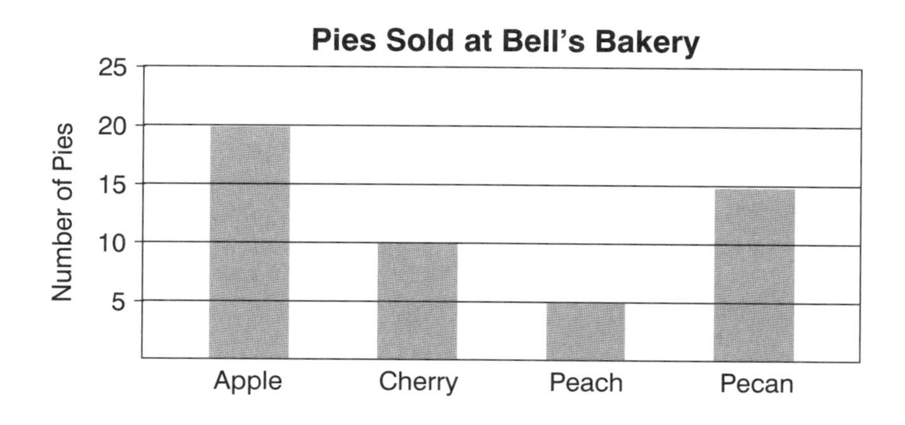

1. How many peach pies sold? __________
2. Which kind sold best? __________
3. How many more pecan pies sold than cherry? __________
4. How many more pecan pies sold than peach pies? __________

❖ Extra: Can you do this? ❖

How many pies sold altogether? __________

148

Trace the rule and copy it.

16 ounces = 1 pound

_____ __________ = _____ __________

Write the time.

Answer these subtraction problems. Do not borrow.

1,635 - 824	1,378 - 536	1,674 - 761	1,498 - 526	1,679 - 865
1,565 - 723	1,585 - 672	1,385 - 413	1,588 - 774	1,687 - 832

Speed Drill

$15 - 7 \quad 16 - 8 \quad 8 + 8 \quad 15 - 8 \quad 7 + 8 \quad 8 + 8$

$15 - 8 \quad 15 - 7 \quad 8 + 8 \quad 8 + 7 \quad 15 - 7 \quad 7 + 8$

"Giving
all diligence . . ."
2 Peter 1:5

$8 + 8 \quad 15 - 7 \quad 8 + 8 \quad 7 + 8 \quad 15 - 8 \quad 8 + 8 \quad 16 - 8 \quad 15 - 7$

$16 - 8 \quad 8 + 8 \quad 8 + 7 \quad 16 - 8 \quad 7 + 8 \quad 8 + 8 \quad 16 - 8 \quad 15 - 8$

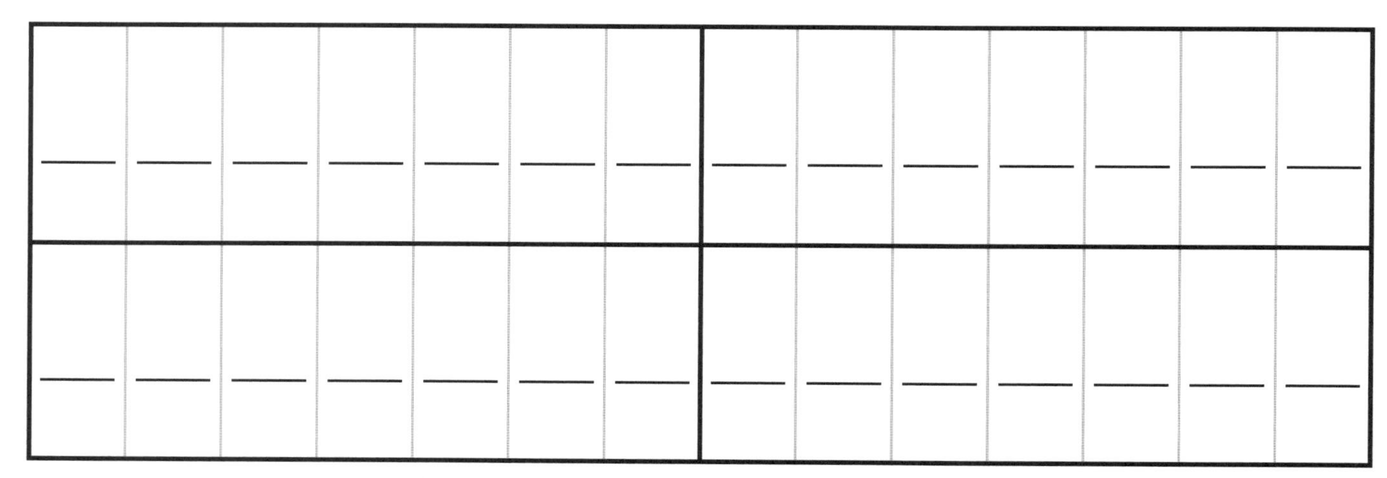

Trace the Addition Family 16.

$$\begin{array}{r}6\\+10\\\hline16\end{array}\quad\begin{array}{r}7\\+9\\\hline16\end{array}\quad\begin{array}{r}8\\+8\\\hline16\end{array}\quad\begin{array}{r}9\\+7\\\hline16\end{array}\quad\begin{array}{r}10\\+6\\\hline16\end{array}$$

Trace the Subtraction Family 16.

$$\begin{array}{r}16\\-6\\\hline10\end{array}\quad\begin{array}{r}16\\-7\\\hline9\end{array}\quad\begin{array}{r}16\\-8\\\hline8\end{array}\quad\begin{array}{r}16\\-9\\\hline7\end{array}\quad\begin{array}{r}16\\-10\\\hline6\end{array}$$

Copy the Addition Family 16.

Copy the Subtraction Family 16.

Make the picture fit the fact.

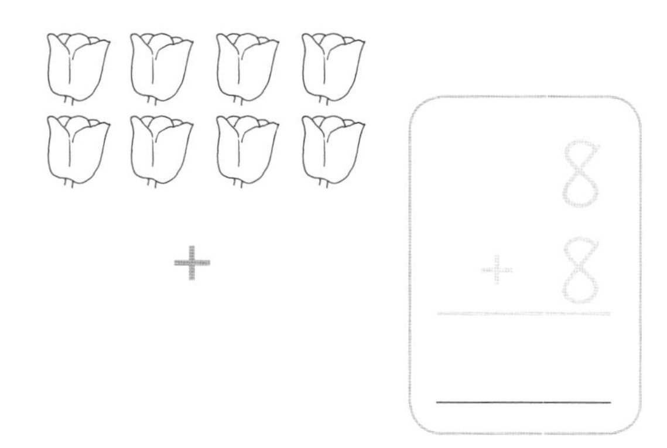

Make the picture fit the fact.

Fill in the missing whole or part. Watch the signs! 

$\begin{array}{r}9\\+\ \ \\\hline16\end{array}$	$\begin{array}{r}\\+10\\\hline16\end{array}$	$\begin{array}{r}8\\+\ \ \\\hline16\end{array}$	$\begin{array}{r}\\+7\\\hline16\end{array}$	$\begin{array}{r}16\\-\ \ \\\hline10\end{array}$	$\begin{array}{r}16\\-\ \ \\\hline7\end{array}$	$\begin{array}{r}16\\-6\\\hline\ \end{array}$	$\begin{array}{r}16\\-\ \ \\\hline8\end{array}$

Answer these addition facts.

8 + 5	9 + 7	6 + 8	10 + 6	3 + 9	8 + 7	5 + 6	8 + 8
4 + 6	6 + 9	5 + 5	9 + 4	7 + 9	8 + 4	6 + 10	8 + 3
4 + 7	10 + 6	7 + 6	6 + 6	5 + 9	3 + 7	8 + 8	2 + 9

Answer these subtraction facts.

13 - 4	16 - 7	11 - 3	14 - 6	16 - 6	10 - 5	12 - 4	15 - 9
11 - 5	15 - 7	12 - 5	16 - 10	13 - 5	15 - 8	10 - 4	16 - 6
12 - 3	10 - 3	16 - 9	13 - 6	11 - 4	15 - 6	10 - 2	12 - 6

149 Round these numbers to the nearest ten.

1. Think—Is it closer to 20 or 30?

22 ☐ 29 ☐ 27 ☐ 23 ☐

2. Think—Is it closer to 50 or 60?

58 ☐ 56 ☐ 51 ☐ 54 ☐

Answer these story problems.

The Bible has many books in it. The Old Testament has 39 books. The New Testament has 27. What is the total number of books in the Bible?

The Old Testament has 39 books and the New Testament has 27. How many more books are in the Old Testament than in the New Testament?

In the book called Genesis, there are 50 chapters. 13 of them tell the story of Joseph. How many chapters are left to tell other stories?

In the Bible, a man named Ziba had fifteen sons and twenty servants. How many people could help Ziba?

Write a fraction for the shaded part of each picture.
Circle the pictures that show fractions the same as $\frac{1}{2}$.

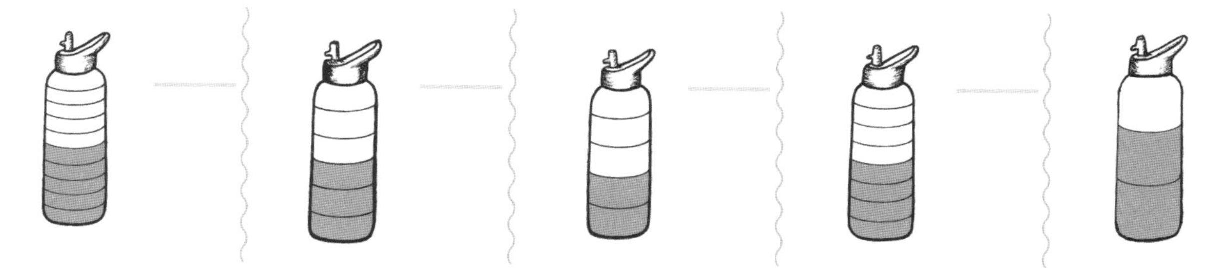

Trace and finish the rule.

16 ounces = ______ ______________

Count the money. Write the amount.

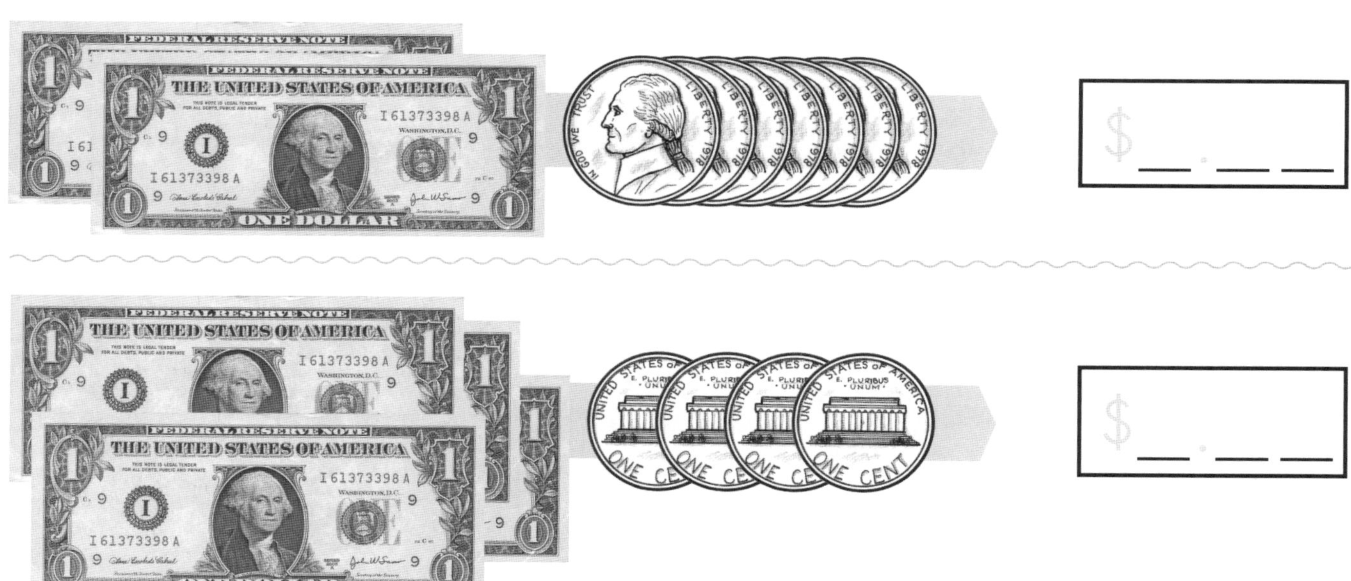

❖ Extra: Can you do this? ❖

Fill in the whole and the parts.

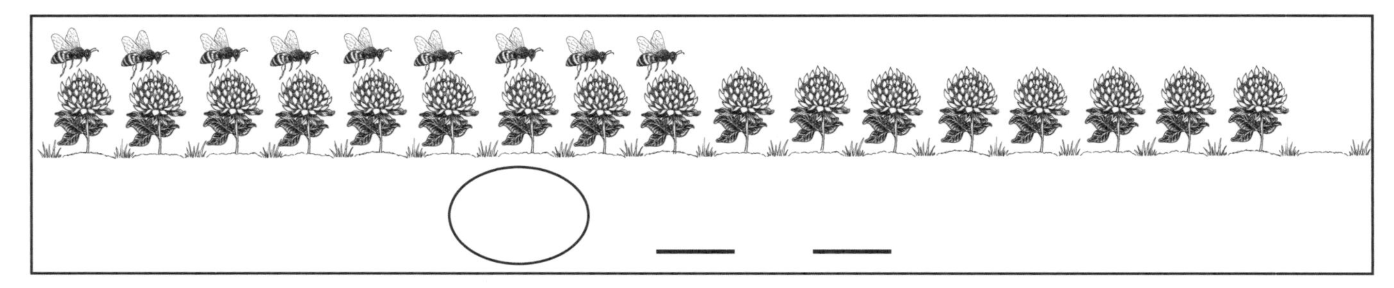

Write a fact for each picture.

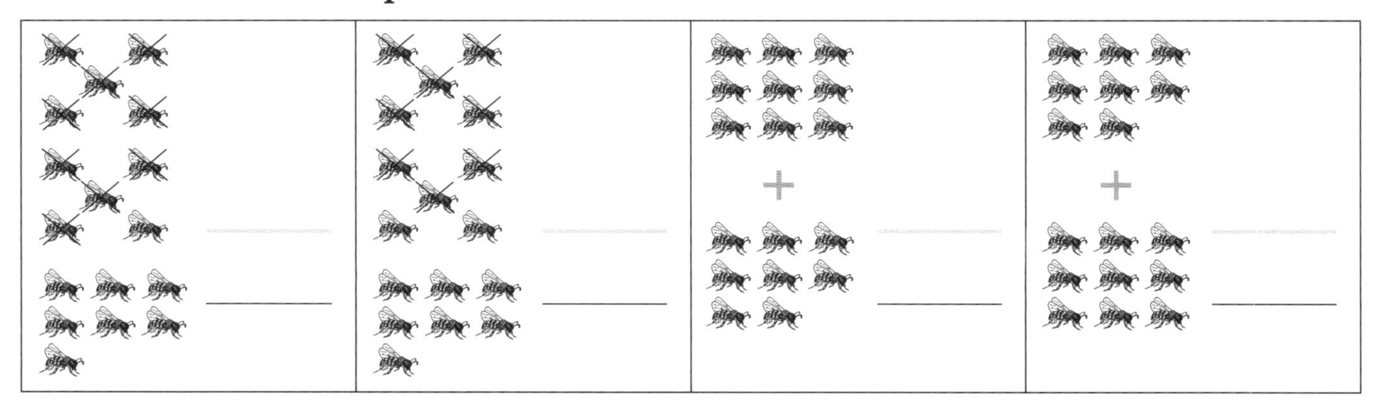

Trace and copy the triplet. Write the facts twice in the hives.

"How sweet are thy words unto my taste! Yea, sweeter than honey to my mouth!"
Psalm 119:103

Answer these facts.

9 + 8 =	17 − 9 =	17 − 8 =	9 + 7 =	8 + 9 =	15 − 7 =	17 − 9 =	17 − 8 =
15 − 6 =	8 + 9 =	9 + 8 =	17 − 8 =	9 + 8 =	16 − 7 =	17 − 9 =	8 + 8 =
17 − 8 =	9 + 8 =	16 − 9 =	17 − 9 =	8 + 8 =	8 + 9 =	15 − 8 =	9 + 8 =
17 − 9 =	17 − 8 =	7 + 8 =	9 + 8 =				

If it's 1 child on a swing
Or 17 bees on wing,
*"His eye seeth
every precious thing."*
If it's 700 toads in spring,
Or 800 birds that sing,
*"His eye seeth
every precious thing."*

Answer these problems. Borrow when you need to.

94 − 56 =	96 − 28 =	76 − 69 =	98 − 28 =	87 − 19 =	85 − 47 =
38 − 2 =	97 − 3 =	51 − 9 =	29 − 5 =	55 − 6 =	72 − 9 =

150

Round these numbers to the nearest ten.

52 ☐	17 ☐	49 ☐	98 ☐
38 ☐	64 ☐	71 ☐	23 ☐

Study the bar graph and answer the questions.

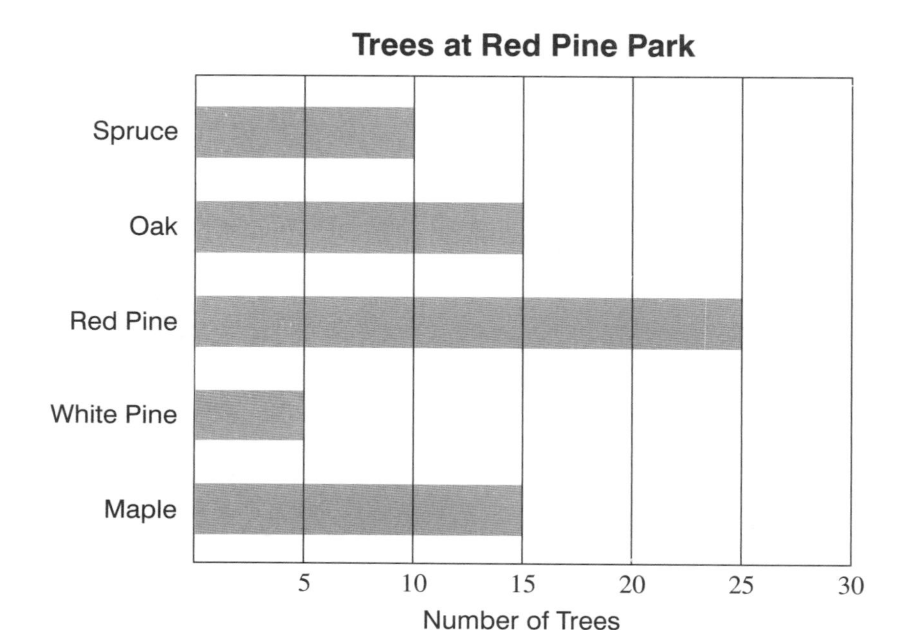

1. How many maple trees are there? ______________

2. Which kind has the same number as maple? ______________

3. How many more red pine trees than white pine trees are there? ________

4. Red pine, white pine and spruce are all evergreen trees. How many evergreens are in the park? ________

5. Why do you think the park is called Red Pine Park?

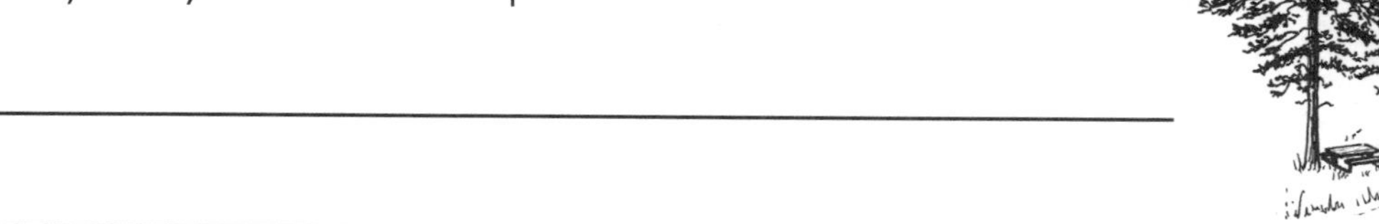

____

____

Speed Drill

"Giving all diligence . . ."
2 Peter 1:5

14	16	16	15	15	16
- 7	- 7	- 8	- 8	- 9	- 9

15	16	16	16	15	16
- 7	- 7	- 8	- 9	- 6	- 8

16	16	15	15	16	15	16	15
- 9	- 8	- 6	- 7	- 8	- 8	- 7	- 6

6	2	7	4	4	3	6	8
3	7	1	4	5	5	2	1
+ 5	+ 7	+ 4	+ 7	+ 2	+ 6	+ 8	+ 4

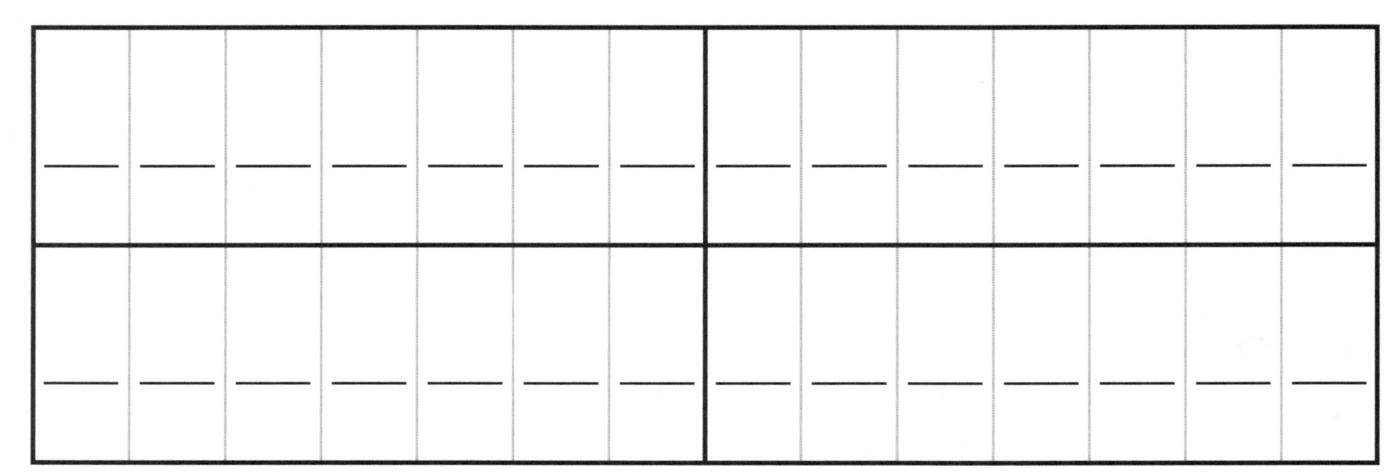

151 **Fill in the whole and the parts.**

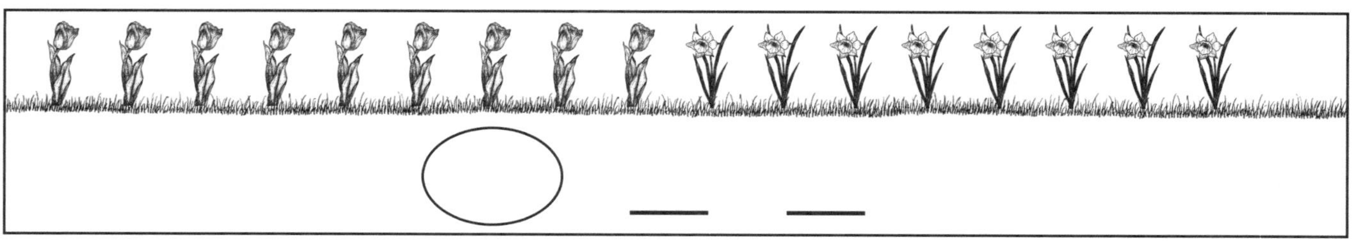

Answer the facts. Make the pictures fit the facts.
Your tulip can look like this one.

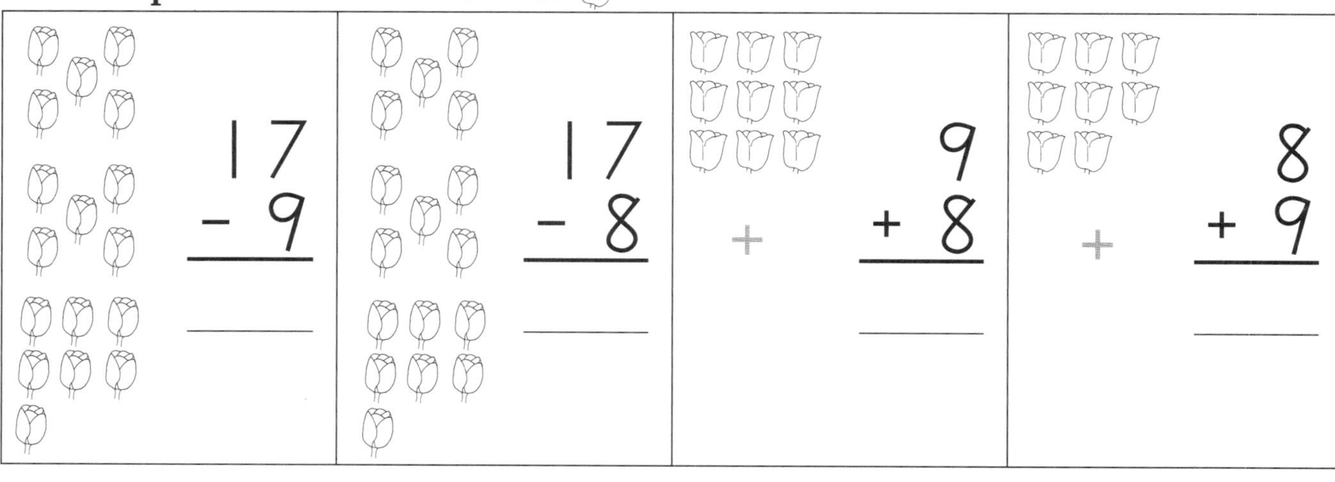

Trace and copy the triplet.

Write the four facts twice.

God, make my life
a little flower
that giveth joy to all.
—Matilda B. B. Edwards

Answer these facts.

17	9	9	17	15	9	14	8
− 8	+ 7	+ 8	− 9	− 8	+ 8	− 7	+ 9

8	9	8	17	16	8	17	16
+ 9	+ 8	+ 8	− 8	− 7	+ 9	− 9	− 8

17	7	8	17	7	9	8	17
− 9	+ 7	+ 9	− 8	+ 9	+ 8	+ 7	− 8

16	14	17	6	17	9
− 9	− 9	− 9	+ 9	− 8	+ 8

Answer these problems. Carry when you need to.

178	69	84	54	145	177
− 86	+ 28	+ 89	+ 95	− 64	− 92

167	76	178	58	83	139
− 75	+ 73	− 97	+ 39	+ 90	− 54

151 **Round these numbers to the nearest ten.**

25 ☐ 65 ☐ 97 ☐ 75 ☐

45 ☐ 82 ☐ 85 ☐ 59 ☐

Answer these story problems.

Fred has 79¢ in his bank. Lee has 58¢ in his bank. How many cents do both boys have?

$__.__ __

James had a box of 24 crayons. He saw that only 18 crayons were in the box. He hunted for the missing crayons. How many was he looking for?

Seventeen bees buzz inside red tulips. Then eight bees fly back to the hive. How many bees are still inside red tulips?

Trace and finish the rules.

____ __________ = 1 pound

4 quarts = ____ __________

____ __________ = 1 foot

7 days = ____ __________

Answer these questions. Think carefully.

1. The loaf of bread weighed 1 pound. How many ounces was that?

   ____ __________

2. Henry was sick for 1 week. For how many days was Henry sick?

   ____ __________

3. The motto was 1 foot wide. How many inches wide was that?

   ____ __________

4. The jug of oil held 1 gallon. How many quarts were in the jug?

   ____ __________

152 **Fill in the whole and the parts. Write the facts.**

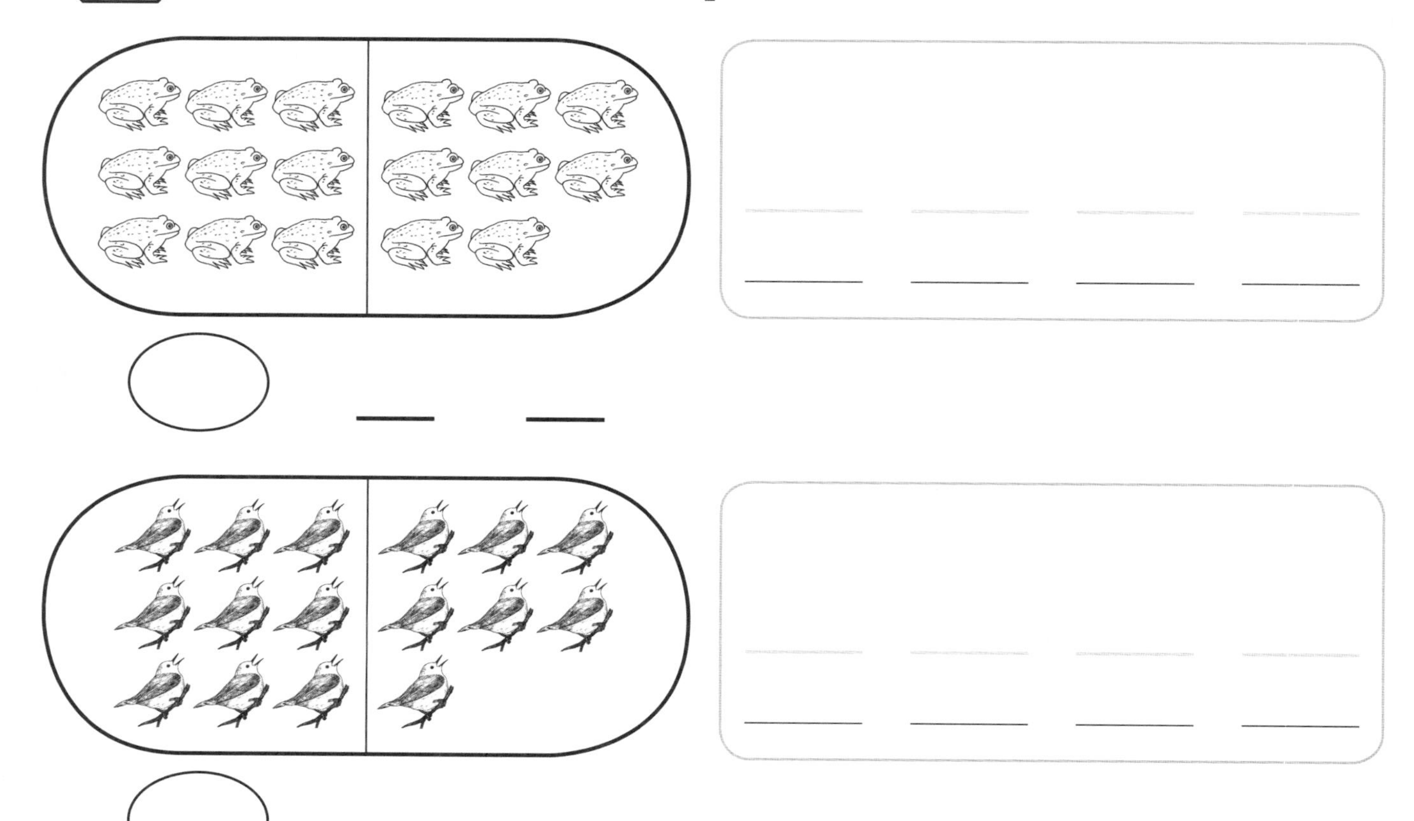

Fill in the missing whole or part.

17 − ___ = 9	___ + 9 = 17	16 − ___ = 9
___ − 9 = 7	8 + ___ = 17	___ − 8 = 9
___ + 8 = 17	9 + 7 = ___	9 + ___ = 17
7 + ___ = 16	___ − 9 = 8	9 + 8 = ___
9 + 7 = ___	16 − ___ = 7	___ − 7 = 9
17 − ___ = 8	___ + 9 = 17	17 − ___ = 8

Answer these problems. Carry or borrow in every problem.

97	76	88	88	97	95
-79	-27	+79	+88	-69	-56
68	76	89	87	76	97
+99	-49	+77	-59	+89	-68
87	86	67	89	87	85
-68	-38	+99	+88	-58	-47

Circle the digit in the tens' place.

56,891   2,504   31,385

78,515   4,970   47,629

Circle the digit in the ten thousands' place.

63,783   1,460   85,199

18,027   9,241   42,508

"And I beheld, and I heard the voice of many angels round about the throne . . .
and the number of them was
ten thousand times ten thousand, and thousands of thousands."

Revelation 5:11

152

Answer these story problems.

Mother plants one dozen plants in the garden and 28 plants in the flower bed. How many plants is that?

_____ _______________

_____ _______________

_____ _______________

Forty-seven children are in the school that Ray attends. Nineteen children are girls. How many children are boys?

_____ _______________

_____ _______________

_____ _______________

Mohan carefully made 38 little round mud balls and let them dry in the sun to use for a marble game. His friend Sebo made 29 mud balls. How many mud balls did they have altogether?

_____ _______________

_____ _______________

_____ _______________

Do these number strings.

15 − 8 + 2 + 8 − 1 = ___

5 + 2 + 3 − 5 + 8 = ___

12 − 9 + 1 + 9 − 5 = ___

3 + 7 − 6 + 3 + 9 = ___

14 − 5 − 2 − 1 + 6 = ___

13 − 9 + 1 + 3 + 8 = ___

Answer these subtraction problems. Borrow once in each problem.

895	679	706	984	867
−149	−493	− 282	−556	−728
___	___	___	___	___

Speed Drill

"Giving all diligence . . ."
2 Peter 1:5

$17 - 9$	$17 - 8$	$9 + 7$	$16 - 9$	$16 - 7$	$8 + 9$
$9 + 8$	$16 - 7$	$17 - 8$	$17 - 9$	$7 + 9$	$16 - 7$

$9 + 8$	$16 - 7$	$8 + 9$	$17 - 8$	$16 - 9$	$9 + 7$	$17 - 8$	$17 - 9$
$17 - 8$	$9 + 8$	$16 - 7$	$7 + 9$	$17 - 9$	$17 - 8$	$16 - 7$	$8 + 9$

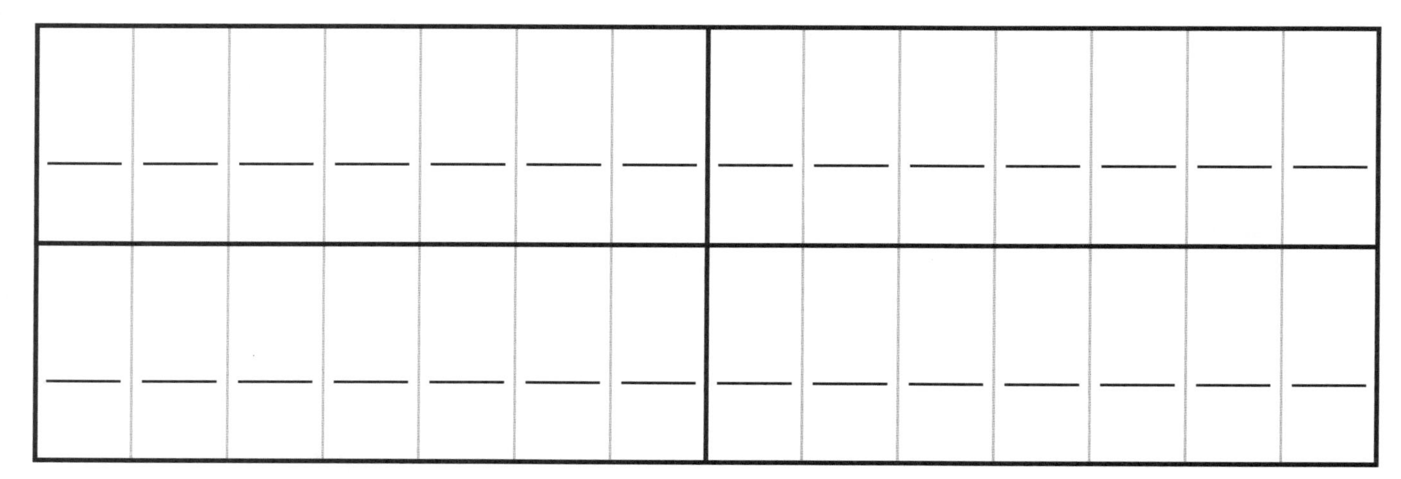

153

Fill in the whole and the parts. Write the facts.

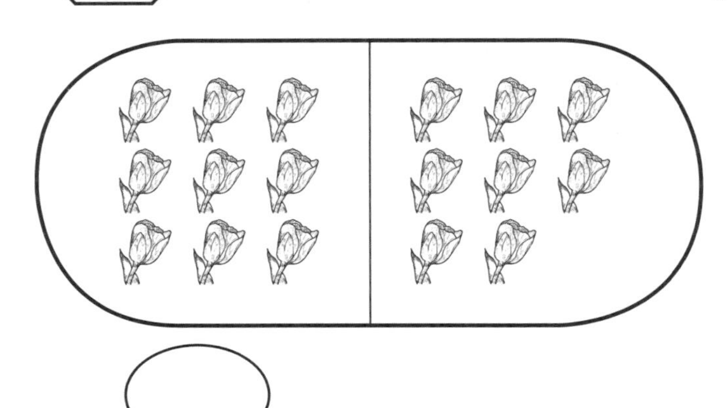

Answer these facts.

$$\begin{array}{r} 16 \\ -\ 8 \\ \hline \end{array} \quad \begin{array}{r} 9 \\ +\ 4 \\ \hline \end{array} \quad \begin{array}{r} 17 \\ -\ 9 \\ \hline \end{array} \quad \begin{array}{r} 9 \\ +\ 6 \\ \hline \end{array} \quad \begin{array}{r} 14 \\ -\ 7 \\ \hline \end{array} \quad \begin{array}{r} 8 \\ +\ 9 \\ \hline \end{array} \quad \begin{array}{r} 7 \\ +\ 8 \\ \hline \end{array} \quad \begin{array}{r} 14 \\ -\ 9 \\ \hline \end{array}$$

$$\begin{array}{r} 9 \\ +\ 8 \\ \hline \end{array} \quad \begin{array}{r} 13 \\ -\ 8 \\ \hline \end{array} \quad \begin{array}{r} 14 \\ -\ 8 \\ \hline \end{array} \quad \begin{array}{r} 9 \\ +\ 7 \\ \hline \end{array} \quad \begin{array}{r} 8 \\ +\ 5 \\ \hline \end{array} \quad \begin{array}{r} 17 \\ -\ 8 \\ \hline \end{array} \quad \begin{array}{r} 8 \\ +\ 7 \\ \hline \end{array} \quad \begin{array}{r} 13 \\ -\ 7 \\ \hline \end{array}$$

$$\begin{array}{r} 13 \\ -\ 9 \\ \hline \end{array} \quad \begin{array}{r} 16 \\ -\ 7 \\ \hline \end{array} \quad \begin{array}{r} 5 \\ +\ 9 \\ \hline \end{array} \quad \begin{array}{r} 9 \\ +\ 8 \\ \hline \end{array} \quad \begin{array}{r} 15 \\ -\ 7 \\ \hline \end{array} \quad \begin{array}{r} 8 \\ +\ 8 \\ \hline \end{array} \quad \begin{array}{r} 6 \\ +\ 9 \\ \hline \end{array} \quad \begin{array}{r} 8 \\ +\ 6 \\ \hline \end{array}$$

$$\begin{array}{r} 15 \\ -\ 6 \\ \hline \end{array} \quad \begin{array}{r} 7 \\ +\ 6 \\ \hline \end{array} \quad \begin{array}{r} 17 \\ -\ 8 \\ \hline \end{array} \quad \begin{array}{r} 7 \\ +\ 7 \\ \hline \end{array} \quad \begin{array}{r} 16 \\ -\ 9 \\ \hline \end{array} \quad \begin{array}{r} 13 \\ -\ 5 \\ \hline \end{array} \quad \begin{array}{r} 15 \\ -\ 8 \\ \hline \end{array} \quad \begin{array}{r} 8 \\ +\ 9 \\ \hline \end{array}$$

Answer these problems. Carry or borrow in every problem.

39 + 38	92 − 73	54 + 58	67 + 47	97 − 58	66 − 58
88 + 89	97 − 19	77 + 99	95 − 27	89 + 86	96 − 38
94 − 15	86 − 69	56 + 48	43 + 79	77 − 38	95 − 87

Study the bar graph and answer the questions.

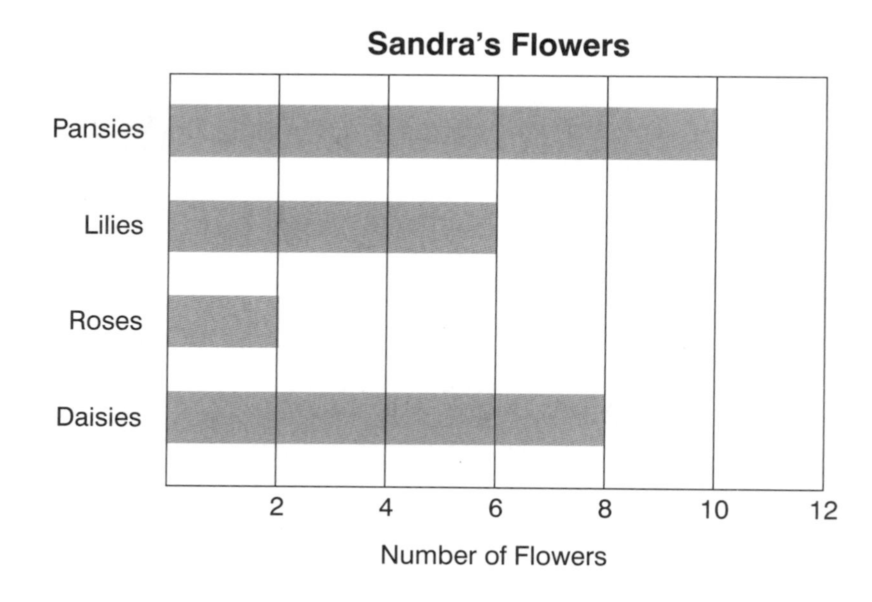

1. Sandra has the most

   ______________________.

2. How many less roses than lilies are there?

   ____

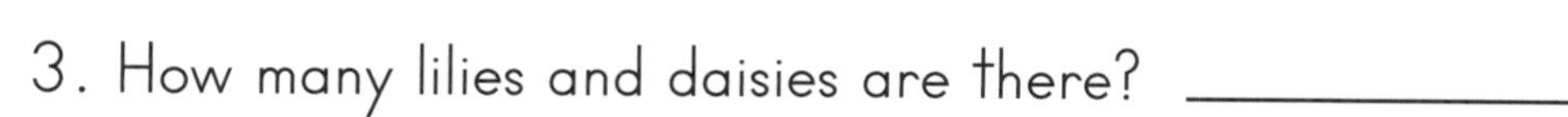

3. How many lilies and daisies are there? ______________

4. How many lilies and roses are there? ______________

153

Round these numbers to the nearest ten.

59 ☐ 35 ☐ 84 ☐ 92 ☐

15 ☐ 71 ☐ 96 ☐ 45 ☐

Trace and finish the rules.

_____ __________ = 1 hour

16 ounces = _____ __________

_____ __________ = 1 foot

Answer these questions. Think carefully.

Martha's cake needs to bake for $\frac{1}{2}$ hour. How many minutes should the cake bake?

____

Samuel and John raked the yard for 1 hour. How many minutes did they rake?

____

The cereal box is 1 foot tall. How many inches tall is the box?

____

The pack of nuts weighs 1 pound. How many ounces does it weigh?

____

Count the money. Add the amounts.

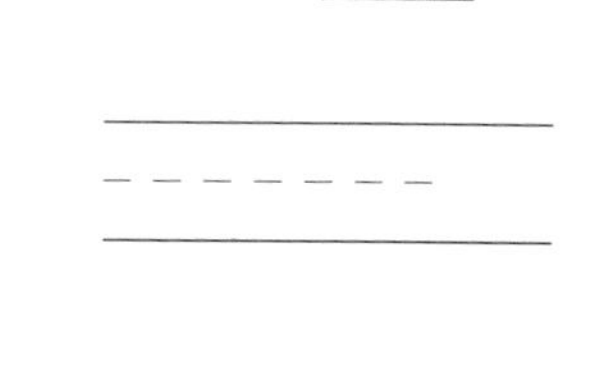

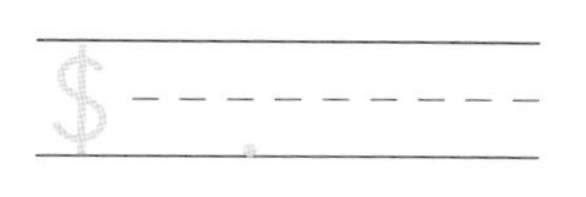

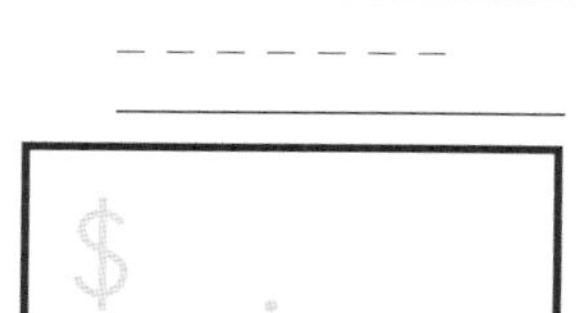

❖ Extra: Can you do these? ❖

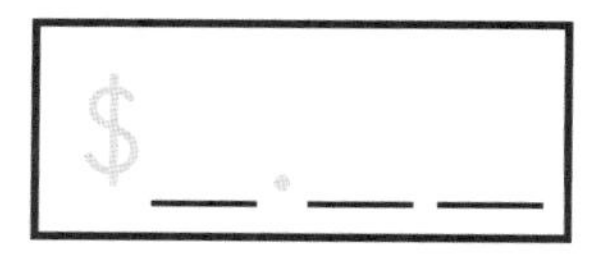

154 Write a fact and a triplet for each picture.

+

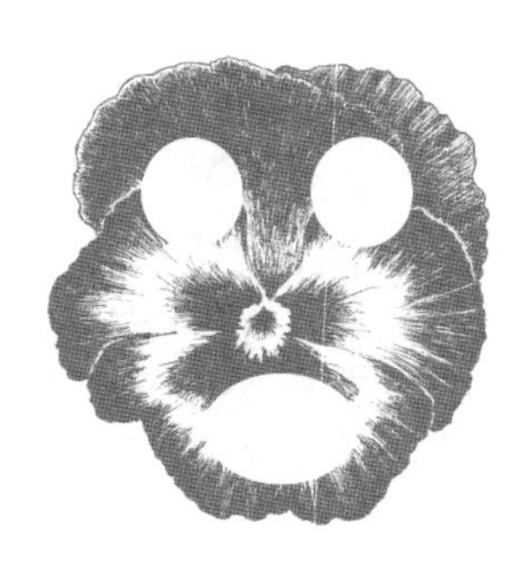

+

Answer these facts.

15 − 8 = ___	9 + 3 = ___	17 − 9 = ___	8 + 8 = ___	5 + 8 = ___	8 + 9 = ___	14 − 8 = ___	7 + 7 = ___
9 + 5 = ___	17 − 8 = ___	6 + 7 = ___	15 − 6 = ___	7 + 9 = ___	14 − 7 = ___	8 + 7 = ___	9 + 8 = ___
16 − 8 = ___	12 − 5 = ___	8 + 9 = ___	14 − 5 = ___	8 + 6 = ___	17 − 8 = ___	13 − 9 = ___	9 + 6 = ___

Answer these problems.

35 43 +79	47 31 +64	15 63 +96	44 13 +66	45 42 +48	63 23 +78
65 24 +78	45 22 +93	32 56 +28	53 22 +95	40 49 +78	36 53 +28
24 54 +96	43 42 +57	45 34 +78	55 22 +87	25 24 +86	25 23 +75

Round these numbers to the nearest ten.

76 ☐ 22 ☐ 98 ☐ 35 ☐

14 ☐ 67 ☐ 55 ☐ 83 ☐

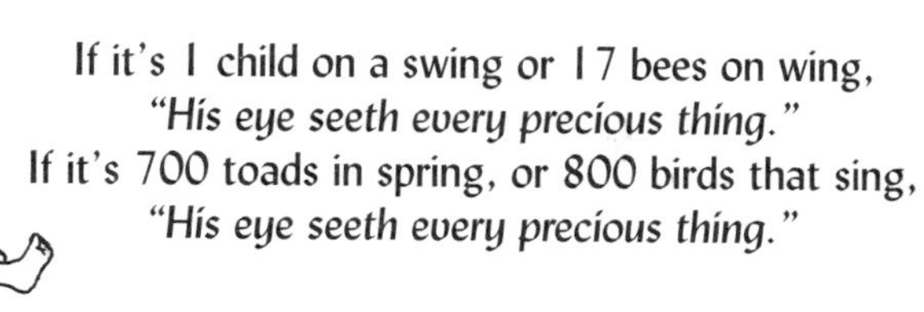

If it's 1 child on a swing or 17 bees on wing,
"His eye seeth every precious thing."
If it's 700 toads in spring, or 800 birds that sing,
"His eye seeth every precious thing."

154 Answer these story problems.

Martha read 23 Bible verses one week, 42 verses the next week and 38 verses the following week. How many verses did Martha read in these 3 weeks?

The Sunday morning service lasted 2 hours. How many minutes was that?

Every day Matthew and Aaron gather the eggs. Today Matthew gathered 466 eggs and Aaron gathered 423.

a. How many eggs did they gather together?

b. How many more did Matthew gather than Aaron?

Answer these subtraction problems. Do not borrow.

$$\begin{array}{r}1,497\\-\ 534\\\hline\end{array}\qquad\begin{array}{r}1,168\\-\ 645\\\hline\end{array}\qquad\begin{array}{r}1,759\\-\ 817\\\hline\end{array}\qquad\begin{array}{r}1,587\\-\ 675\\\hline\end{array}\qquad\begin{array}{r}1,389\\-\ 905\\\hline\end{array}$$

Speed Drill

"Giving all diligence . . ."
2 Peter 1:5

$7 + 9 =$ ___ $9 + 8 =$ ___ $17 - 8 =$ ___ $16 - 7 =$ ___ $8 + 8 =$ ___ $17 - 9 =$ ___

$16 - 7 =$ ___ $17 - 9 =$ ___ $9 + 7 =$ ___ $8 + 9 =$ ___ $16 - 8 =$ ___ $16 - 7 =$ ___

$17 - 9 =$ ___ $9 + 8 =$ ___ $17 - 9 =$ ___ $8 + 8 =$ ___ $16 - 7 =$ ___ $17 - 8 =$ ___ $9 + 8 =$ ___ $9 + 7 =$ ___

$8 + 9 =$ ___ $16 - 8 =$ ___ $17 - 8 =$ ___ $17 - 9 =$ ___ $8 + 9 =$ ___ $7 + 9 =$ ___ $17 - 9 =$ ___ $16 - 7 =$ ___

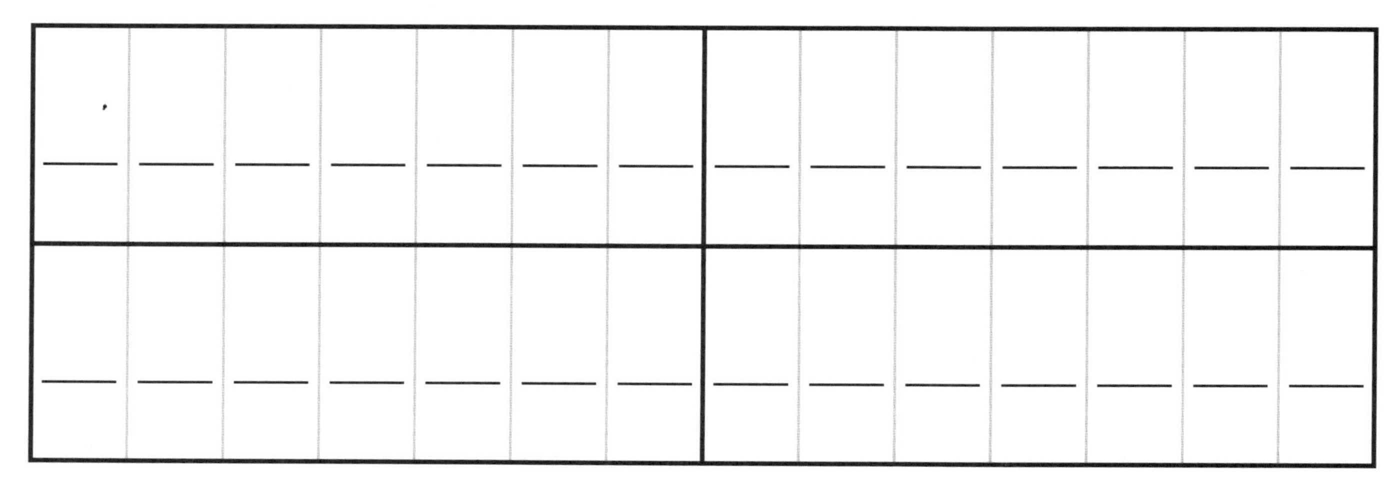

155 Write a fact and a triplet for each picture.

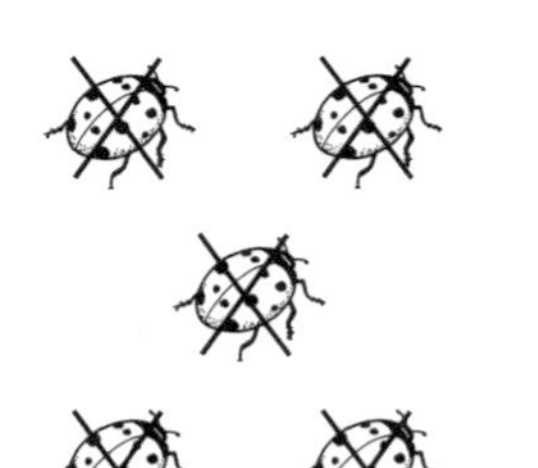

Answer these facts.

8	3	17	9	4	13	6	16
+ 9	+ 8	− 8	+ 8	+ 8	− 8	+ 8	− 8
11	9	13	8	8	10	12	17
− 3	+ 8	− 5	+ 3	+ 8	− 8	− 8	− 9
15	2	16	12	17	8	14	7
− 7	+ 8	− 8	− 4	− 8	+ 5	− 6	+ 8

Answer these problems. Borrow when you need to.

155

97	95	96	99	76	95
-79	-78	-38	-56	-49	-56
___	___	___	___	___	___

97	82	87	96	77	74
-67	-35	-58	-48	-49	-25
___	___	___	___	___	___

67	84	54	93	78	55
-28	-26	-37	-66	-35	-37
___	___	___	___	___	___

Answer these story problems.

Thirty-seven bees buzz. Then a toad eats 8 of them. How many bees are left?

______ ______________

______ ______________

______ ______________

Bees visited 523 dandelions and 271 daffodils. How many flowers was that?

______ ______________

______ ______________

______ ______________

The letter took 1 week and 3 days to come from Uncle Peter's house. How many days did it take?

______ ______________

155

Add commas to the numbers.
Write the digits in the correct places.

	ten thousands	thousands	hundreds	tens	ones
15893					
72614					
3571					
29489					
56306					

Trace and finish the rules.

2 cups = ____ ____________

____ ____________ = 1 gallon

16 ounces = ____ ____________

____ ____________ = $\frac{1}{2}$ dozen

If it's 1 child on a swing or 17 bees on wing,
"His eye seeth every precious thing."
If it's 700 toads in spring, or 800 birds that sing,
"His eye seeth every precious thing."

This is a Line Graph.
It helps us compare grades in Ruth's arithmetic lessons for 10 days.

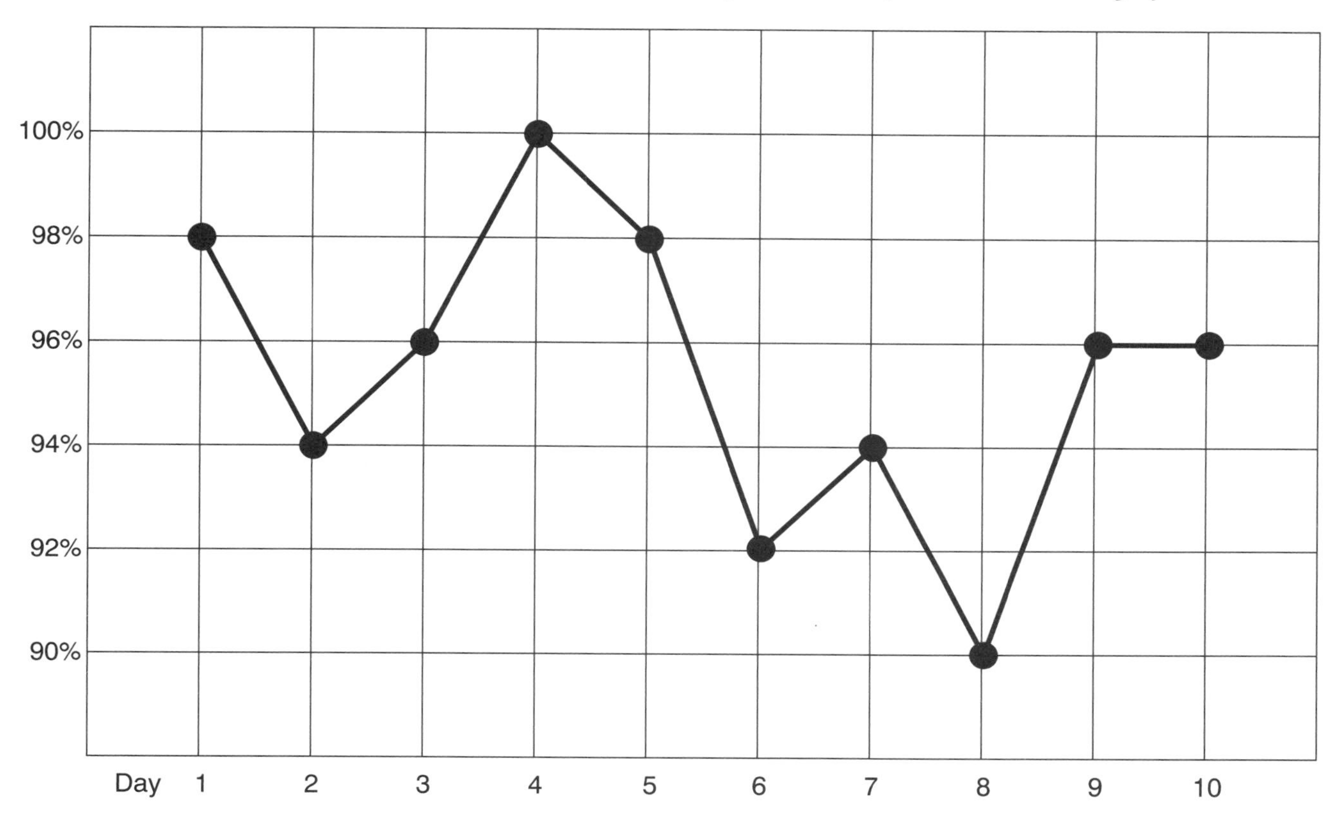

Study the line graph and answer the questions.

1. On which day did Ruth have her highest score? ________________
   What was the score? ________________

2. On which day did Ruth have the lowest score? ________________
   What was the score? ________________

3. On which three days did she have the same score?
   ________________ ________________ ________________

4. What score did Ruth have on day 6? ________________

Trace the Addition Family 17.

7	8	9	10
+ 10	+ 9	+ 8	+ 7
17	17	17	17

Make the picture fit the fact.

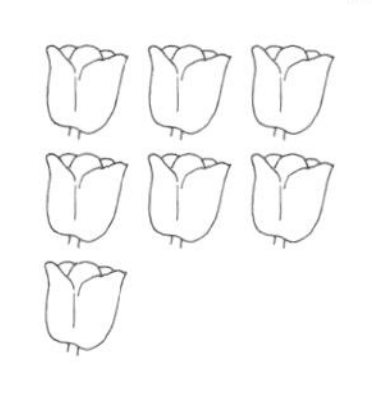

+

Trace the Subtraction Family 17

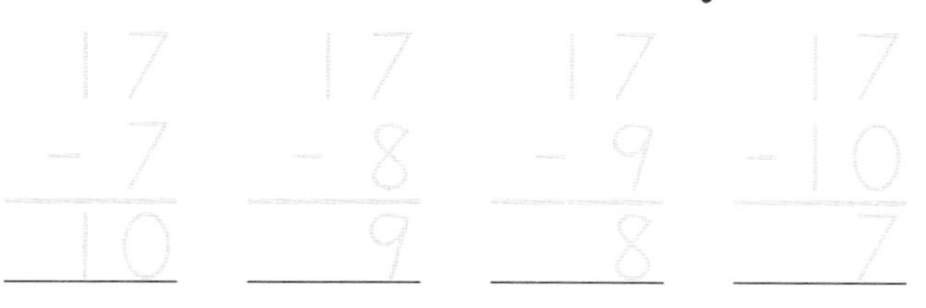

Copy the Addition Family 17.

Copy the Subtraction Family 17.

Make the picture fit the fact.

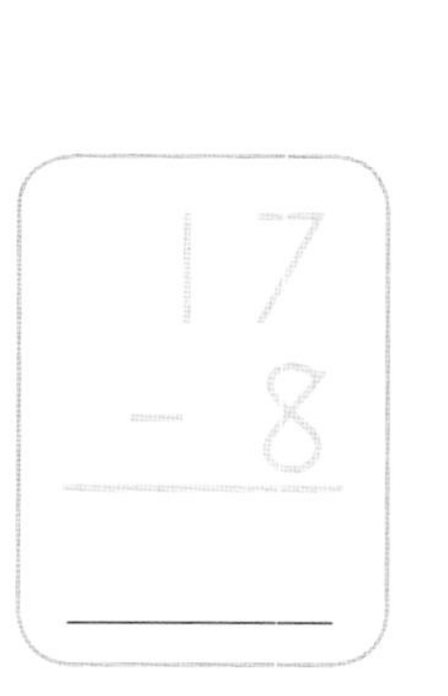

Fill in the missing whole or part. Watch the signs!

8		9	10	17	17	17	17
+	+ 7	+ 8	+	−	− 8	−	−
17	17		17	7		10	9

Answer these addition facts and addition problems.

8	6	7	9	8	5	8	7
+ 8	+ 7	+ 10	+ 5	+ 4	+ 8	+ 9	+ 5

9	10	7	7	9	3	10	4
+ 8	+ 7	+ 8	+ 7	+ 7	+ 9	+ 7	+ 9

825	683	863	867	537
+536	+267	+885	+449	+368

Answer these subtraction facts and subtraction problems.

17	16	14	17	13	12	15	12
- 7	- 8	- 5	- 9	- 8	- 4	- 8	- 7

15	13	17	14	12	16	14	13
- 6	- 4	-10	- 7	- 6	- 9	- 8	- 7

97	70	62	128	178	93
-68	- 2	-58	-36	-92	-88

156 Round these numbers to the nearest ten.

116 ☐	192 ☐	157 ☐	124 ☐
179 ☐	148 ☐	185 ☐	131 ☐

Write a fraction for the shaded part of each picture.

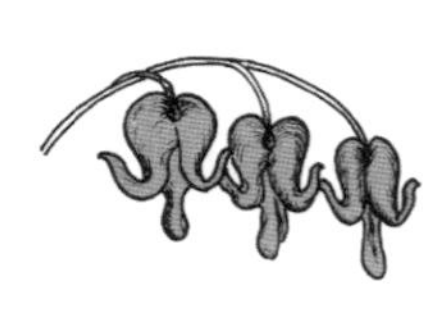    

Write the time.

Speed Drill

"Giving all diligence . . ."
2 Peter 1:5

15	13	12	16	11	12
- 6	- 5	- 6	- 7	- 4	- 3

13	11	17	14	12	16
- 6	- 5	- 9	- 7	- 5	- 8

12	11	17	14	15	13	11	14
- 8	- 3	- 8	- 9	- 7	- 4	- 2	- 6

4	4	4	7	9	5	2	5
5	3	4	2	0	2	6	3
+7	+5	+6	+8	+3	+6	+3	+7

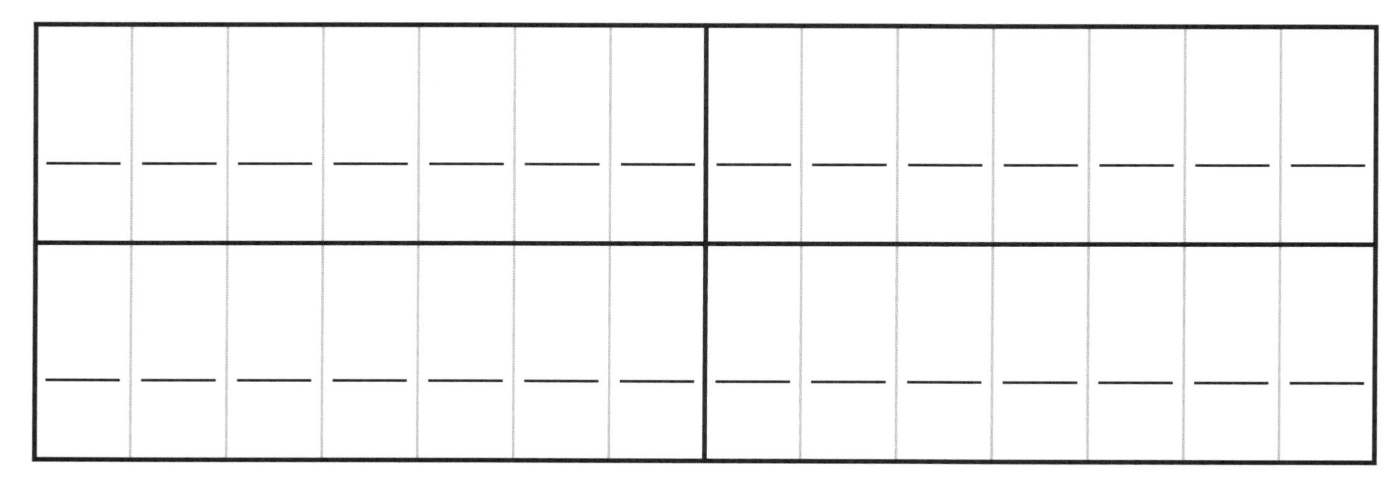

157 Fill in the whole and the parts.

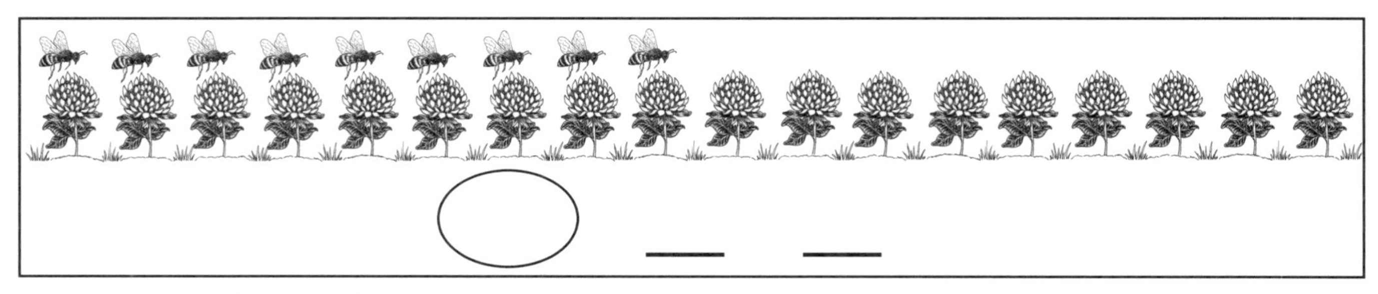

Write a fact for each picture.

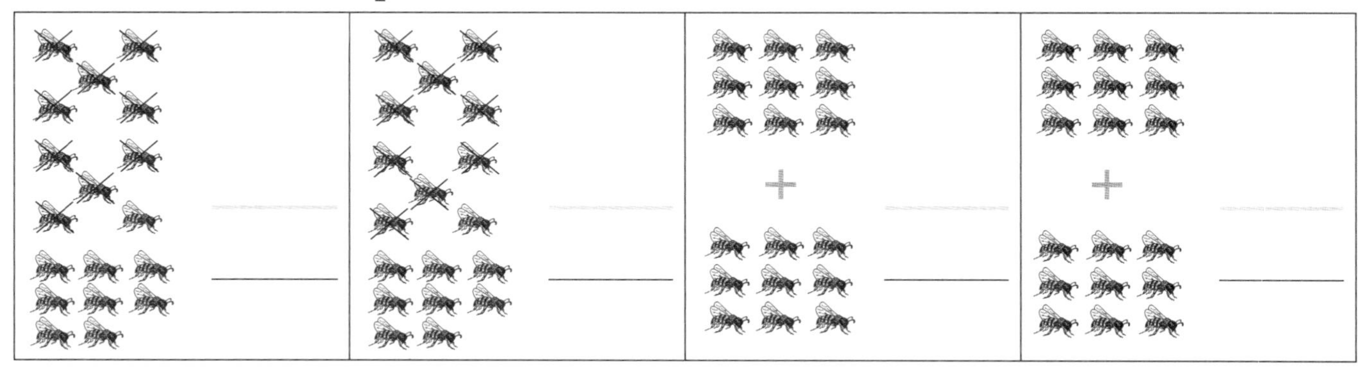

Trace and copy the triplet.

Write the two facts four times each in the honeycomb below.

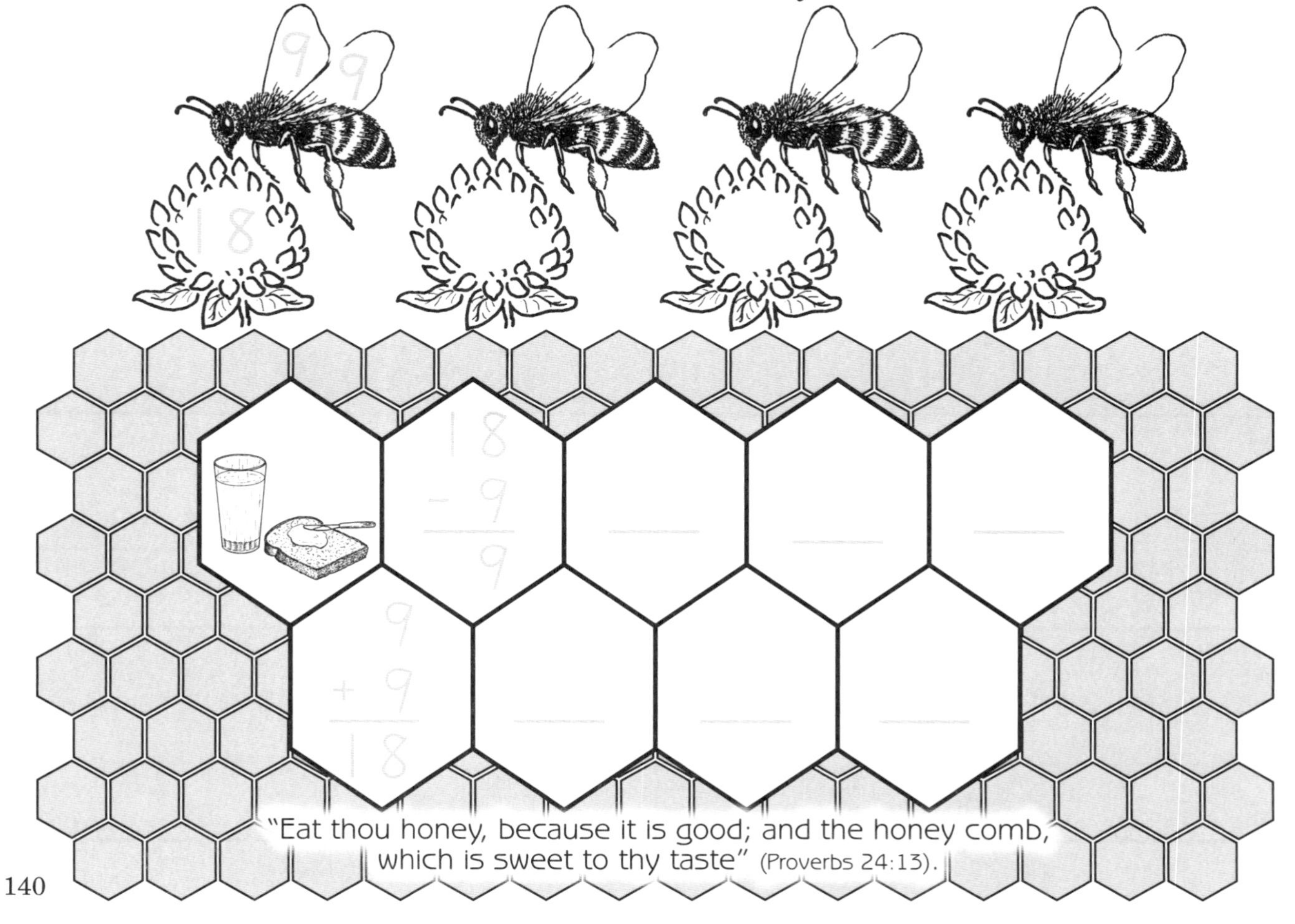

Answer these facts.

$9 + 9 =$ ___ $18 - 9 =$ ___ $9 + 7 =$ ___ $17 - 8 =$ ___ $16 - 8 =$ ___ $18 - 9 =$ ___

$9 + 9 =$ ___ $7 + 9 =$ ___ $8 + 9 =$ ___ $18 - 9 =$ ___ $16 - 9 =$ ___ $9 + 9 =$ ___ $18 - 9 =$ ___ $17 - 9 =$ ___

$17 - 8 =$ ___ $9 + 7 =$ ___ $18 - 9 =$ ___ $16 - 8 =$ ___ $9 + 9 =$ ___ $8 + 8 =$ ___ $18 - 9 =$ ___

Answer these story problems.

Mother made muffins. She made one dozen oatmeal muffins, one dozen blueberry muffins, and one dozen pumpkin muffins. How many muffins did Mother make?

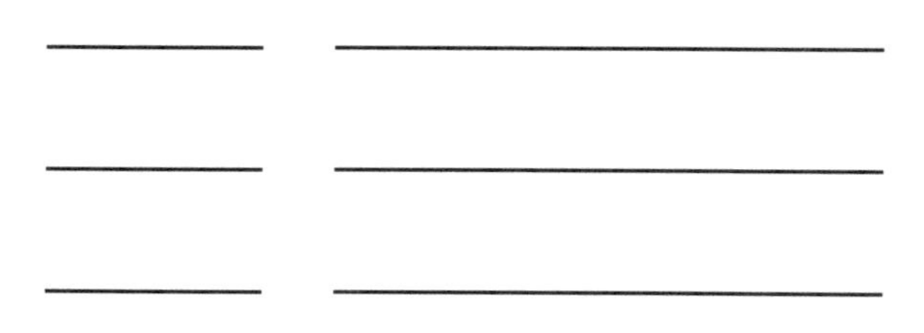

Mother gave eight muffins to Grandmother and kept the rest. How many did Mother keep?

157

Answer these problems. Carry one or two times in each problem.

783	368	459	468	149
+997	+526	+879	+399	+629

438	317	558	448	318
+267	+659	+148	+529	+389

386	929	589	649	276
+394	+849	+278	+689	+618

Round these numbers to the nearest ten.

37 ☐ 163 ☐ 88 ☐ 125 ☐

74 ☐ 119 ☐ 46 ☐ 151 ☐

Do these number strings.

9 + 8 − 7 − 6 + 4 = ___

16 − 8 + 2 + 7 − 9 = ___

8 + 4 − 6 + 8 − 5 = ___

5 + 6 − 9 + 8 + 4 = ___

2 + 3 + 8 − 4 + 9 = ___

9 − 6 + 10 − 6 + 8 = ___

Study the bar graph and answer the questions.

157

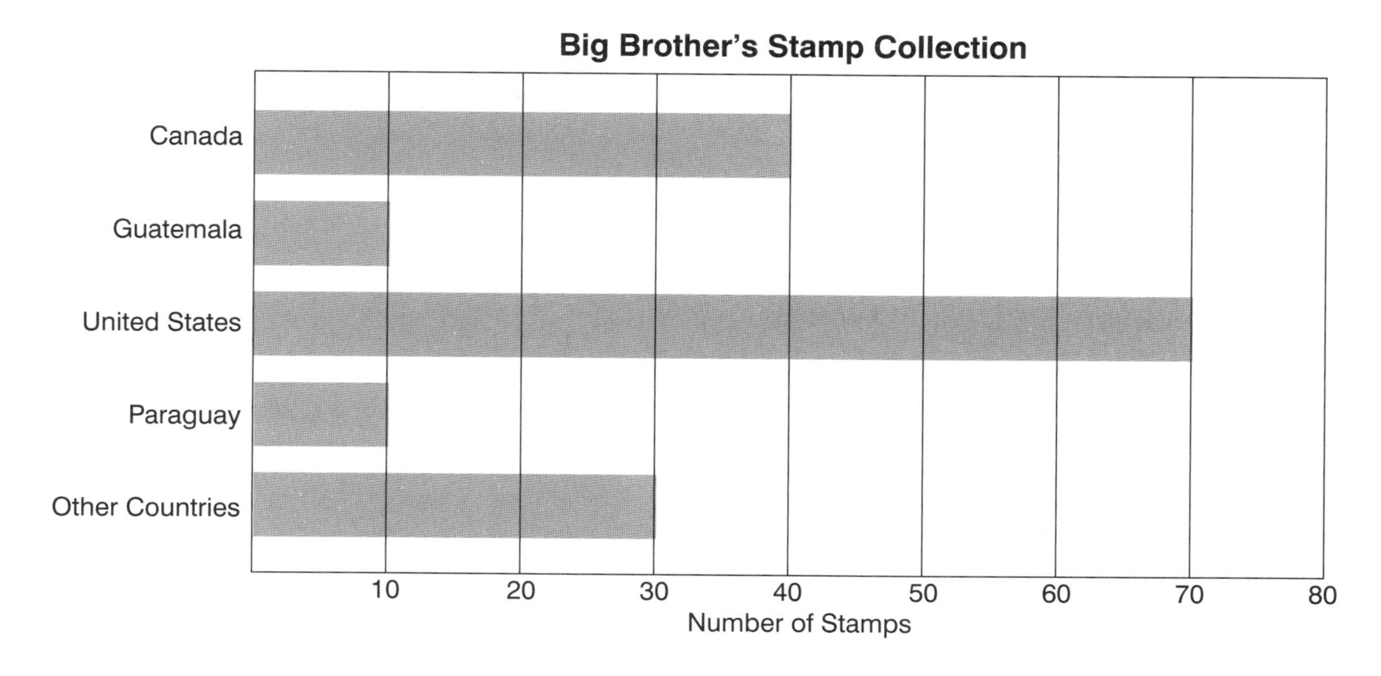

1. What does the graph tell us about?

 ____

2. How many stamps does Big Brother have from the United States?

 ____

3. From which two countries does he have the same number?

 ______________ ______________

4. From which country does he have 40 stamps? ______________

5. How many stamps does Big Brother have from Canada and the United States together? __________

6. How many does he have that are not from Canada or the United States?

 ____

7. How many more does he have from the United States than from Canada?

 ____

158

Fill in the whole and the parts.

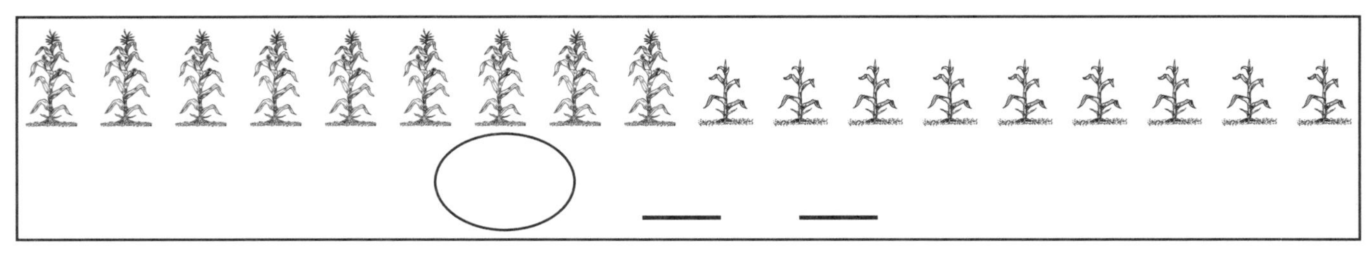

Answer the facts. Make the pictures fit the facts.
Your cloud can look like this one.

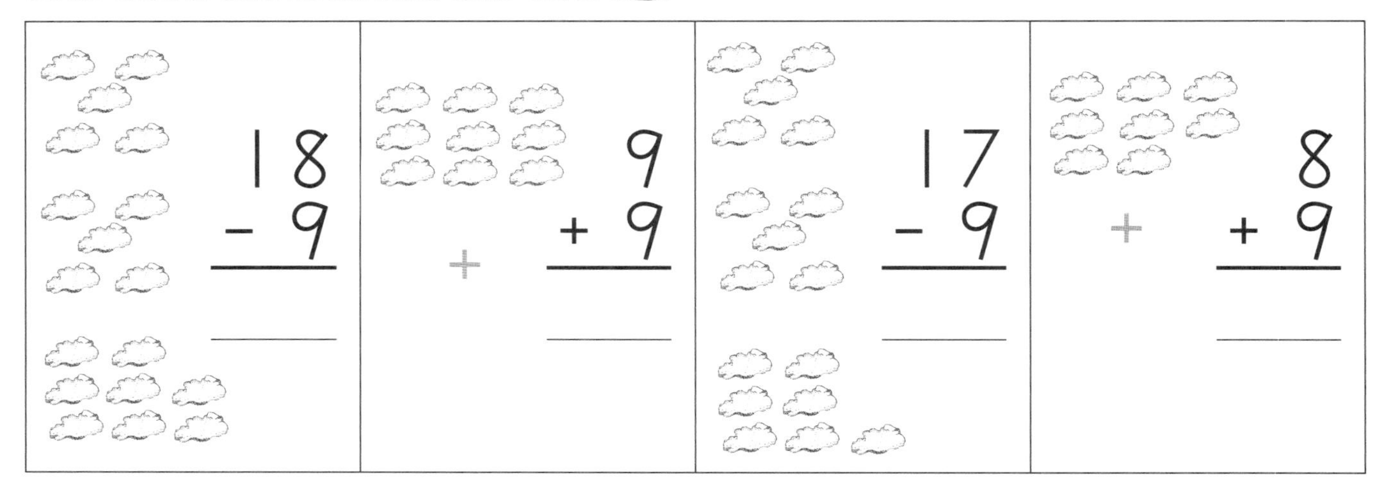

Trace and copy the triplet.

Answer these facts.

$8 + 9$	$18 - 9$	$15 - 6$	$9 + 5$	$9 + 9$	$16 - 9$	$7 + 9$	$9 + 9$
$18 - 9$	$4 + 9$	$9 + 8$	$9 + 9$	$17 - 8$	$13 - 9$	$18 - 9$	$9 + 7$

Answer these facts.

15	9	16	18	9	17
− 9	+ 9	− 7	− 9	+ 6	− 9

18	14	9	18	8	12	9	17
− 9	− 9	+ 3	− 9	+ 9	− 3	+ 9	− 9

12	9	9	11	18	9	9	18
− 9	+ 2	+ 9	− 2	− 9	+ 9	+ 7	− 9

Answer these problems. Carry when you need to.

188	177	168	81	189	69
− 95	− 94	− 97	+ 97	− 97	+ 29

97	184	149	95	68
+ 90	− 94	− 58	+ 82	+ 29

59	187	89	159	179	185
+ 39	− 95	+ 89	− 88	− 96	− 92

158

Answer these story problems.

The Groffs were butchering. Father found that the calf weighed 360 pounds and the hog weighed 335. How many pounds did both animals weigh?

_______ _______________

_______ _______________

_______ _______________

Mae and Fay played store. Mae sold a cup for 59¢ and a bell for 39¢. How many cents was that altogether?

____

____

____

Answer these questions. Think carefully.

1. Visitors drove 1 hour to come to church. How many minutes did they drive? __________ _______________

2. Mary said, "This box of pencils has 1 dozen." The box has __________ pencils.

3. The bucket held 1 gallon of ice cream. How many quarts was that? __________ _______________

4. The teacher's desk is 1 yard and 2 feet long. How many feet long is it? (Think: 1 yard = 3 feet. 3 feet plus 2 more feet = ________ feet long.)

5. Robert weighed a songbook. He said, "This book weighs 1 pound and 2 ounces." How many ounces does the book weigh? (Think: 1 pound = 16 ounces. 16 ounces + 2 more ounces = __________ ounces.)

If it's 1 child on a swing
Or 18 bees on wing,
"His eye seeth every precious thing."
If it's 900 clover tops,
Or 1000 honey drops,
"His eye seeth every precious thing."

Speed Drill

"Giving
all diligence . . ."
2 Peter 1:5

17	18	8	17	9	16
− 8	− 9	+ 8	− 9	+ 9	− 9

18	9	8	16	9	18
− 9	+ 7	+ 9	− 8	+ 8	− 9

16	9	18	17	9	9	16	8
− 7	+ 9	− 9	− 9	+ 7	+ 9	− 8	+ 9

9	7	18	9	16	8	17	9
+ 9	+ 9	− 9	+ 8	− 9	+ 8	− 8	+ 9

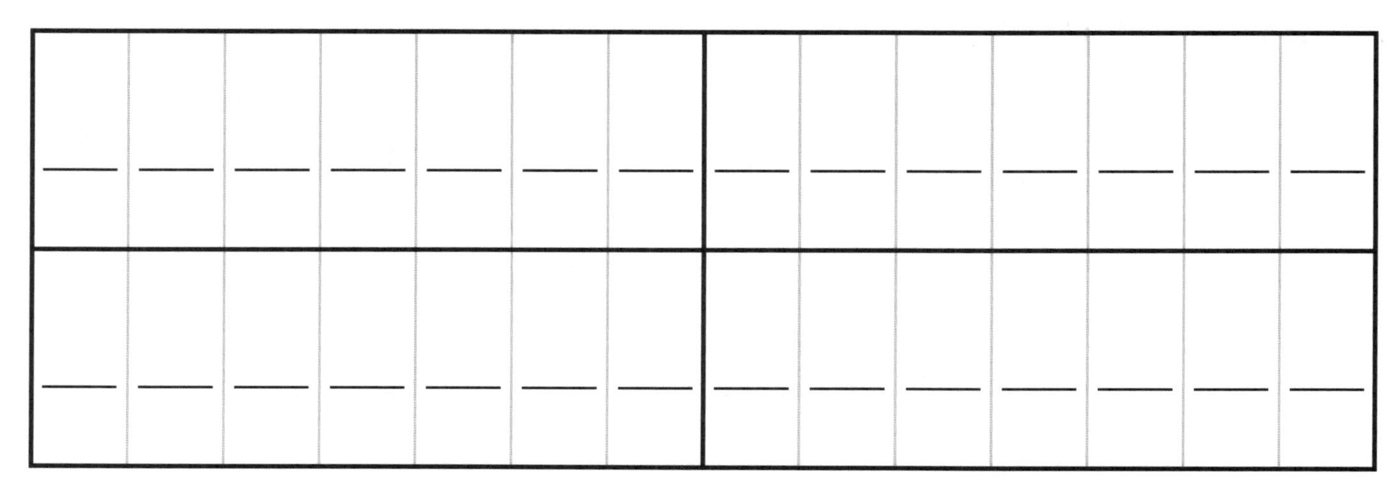

159 Fill in the whole and the parts. Write the facts.

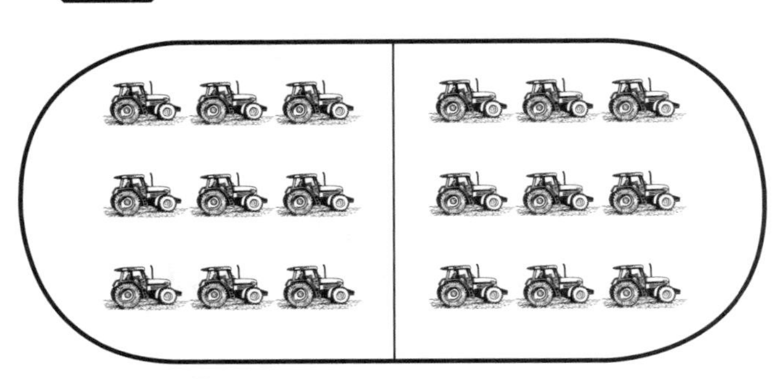

Answer these facts.

17	8	18	6	16	15	9	6
− 9	+ 8	− 9	+ 8	− 9	− 8	+ 9	+ 9

16	14	8	9	15	8	17	7
− 8	− 7	+ 9	+ 9	− 6	+ 7	− 8	+ 9

9	15	16	5	18	9	9	14
+ 8	− 7	− 7	+ 9	− 9	+ 6	+ 9	− 6

Answer these problems. Carry or borrow in every problem.

98 − 59	79 + 47	87 − 48		49 + 58	98 − 69
57 − 19	37 + 79	76 − 39	95 − 58	47 + 69	86 − 48
68 + 58	78 − 39		96 − 57	88 − 59	38 + 69

Write the time.

159 Answer these story problems.

Lee's family drove 88 miles to the zoo and 99 miles to the airport. How many miles was that?

Bruce said, "We have had 159 days of school, and we have 21 more days to go." How many days of school will Bruce have this year?

Mohan used newspaper, palm leaf stems, and rice glue to make a kite. He tried it out and it flew, but he had only 36 feet of string. Later, Father bought 55 feet of string for Mohan to add to his kite string. Now how high can Mohan's kite fly?

Trace and finish the rules.

____ ________ = 1 pound

2 pints = ____ ________

____ ________ = 1 gallon

$\frac{4}{4}$ = ____ ________

This is another line graph.
It shows us how much Daryl grew each year.
Study the line graph and answer the questions.

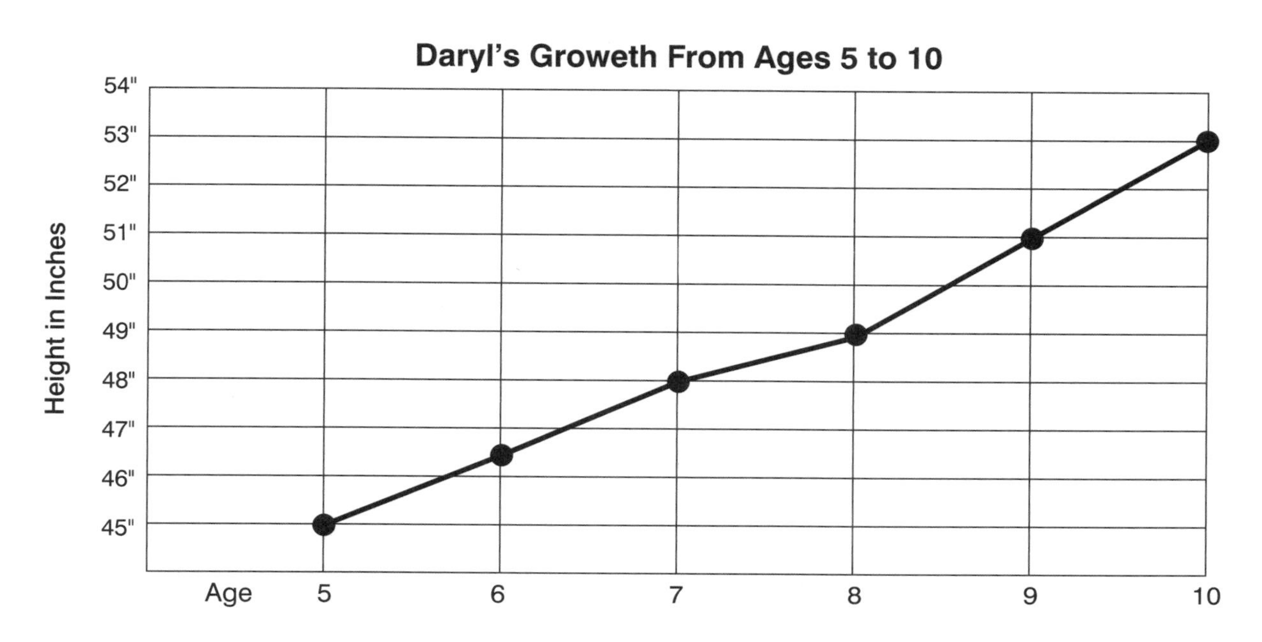

1. What was Daryl's height at age 5? __________

2. What was his height at age 7? __________

3. Look at Daryl's height for age 7 and age 8. How much did he grow?

   ____

4. Now look at his height for age 8 and age 9. How much did he grow?

   ____

5. How tall is Daryl at age 10? __________

❖ Extra: Can you do this? ❖

Use your answer from number 5. Daryl's big brother is 18 inches taller than Daryl is. How tall is Daryl's brother?

Trace the Addition Family 18.

8	9	10
+ 10	+ 9	+ 8
18	18	18

Trace the Subtraction Family 18.

18	18	18
− 8	− 9	− 10
10	9	8

Copy the Addition Family 18.

Copy Subtraction Family 18.

Fill in the missing whole or part.

+ 9 / 18	8 + / 16	10 + / 18	+ 8 / 17	10 + / 17	+ 9 / 18	9 + / 16	9 + / 18
18 − 9 /	18 − / 10	17 − 7 /	16 − / 8	18 − / 9	17 − / 9	18 − 8 /	17 − / 8

Answer these addition problems.

6	2	3	8	2	4	3	5
3	6	5	1	4	5	5	3
+ 9	+ 5	+ 8	+ 9	+ 6	+ 6	+ 9	+ 6
___	___	___	___	___	___	___	___

3	2	4	4	2	3	4	5
6	7	3	5	5	6	2	2
+ 9	+ 7	+ 6	+ 9	+ 7	+ 8	+ 9	+ 5
___	___	___	___	___	___	___	___

Answer these subtraction problems.
Borrow when you need to.

169	92	78	175	159
- 78	- 77	- 69	- 85	- 64
___	___	___	___	___

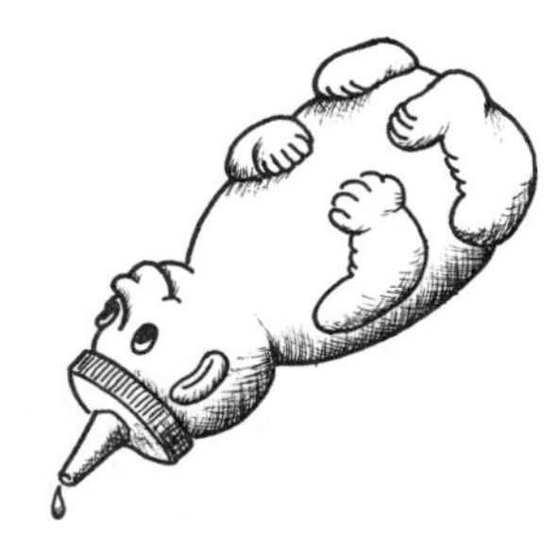

187	90	118	63	60	128
- 92	- 83	- 28	- 54	- 45	- 37
___	___	___	___	___	___

81	48	74	57	92
- 74	- 9	- 5	- 8	- 3
___	___	___	___	___

160 Answer these story problems.

Mother made one dozen tarts. She tucked 9 tarts into lunches. How many tarts were left?

Little lambs run and skip. 19 lambs are black. 18 lambs are white. How many lambs is that altogether?

Round these numbers to the nearest ten.

31 ☐ 145 ☐ 83 ☐ 176 ☐

164 ☐ 98 ☐ 125 ☐ 12 ☐

Write a fraction for the shaded part of each picture.

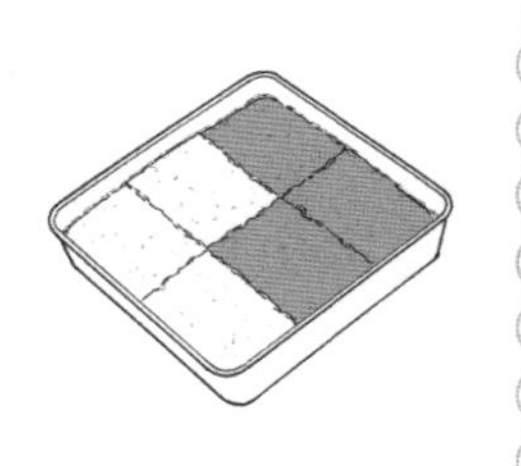

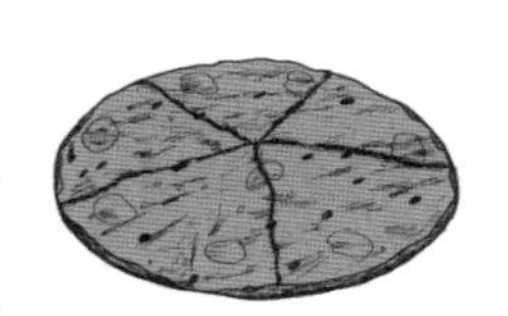

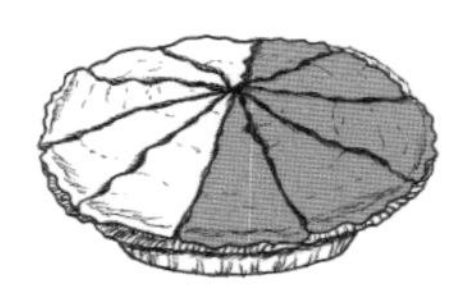

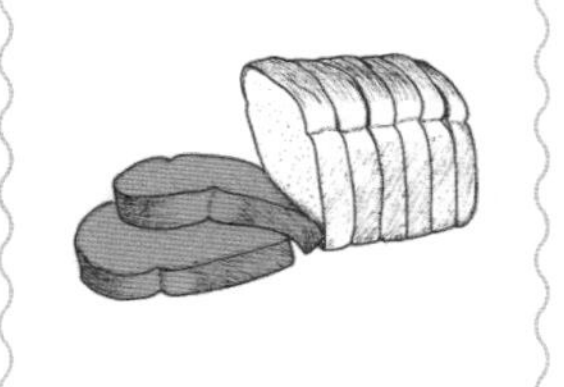

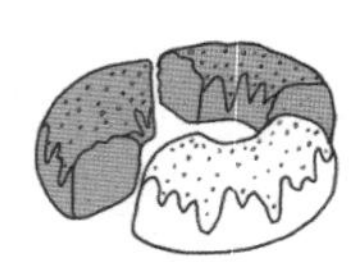

If it's 1 child on a swing
Or 18 bees on wing,
"His eye seeth every precious thing."
If it's 900 clover tops,
Or 1000 honey drops,
"His eye seeth every precious thing."

Speed Drill

"Giving all diligence . . ."
2 Peter 1:5

17	18	16	18	16	15
− 9	− 9	− 9	− 9	− 7	− 9

15	17	15	17	18	16
− 8	− 8	− 7	− 9	− 9	− 9

16	18	15	18	17	15	16	17
− 7	− 9	− 9	− 9	− 8	− 8	− 7	− 9

5	6	5	2	6	3	4	3
4	2	3	7	3	4	5	6
+ 9	+ 9	+ 8	+ 9	+ 9	+ 9	+ 8	+ 9

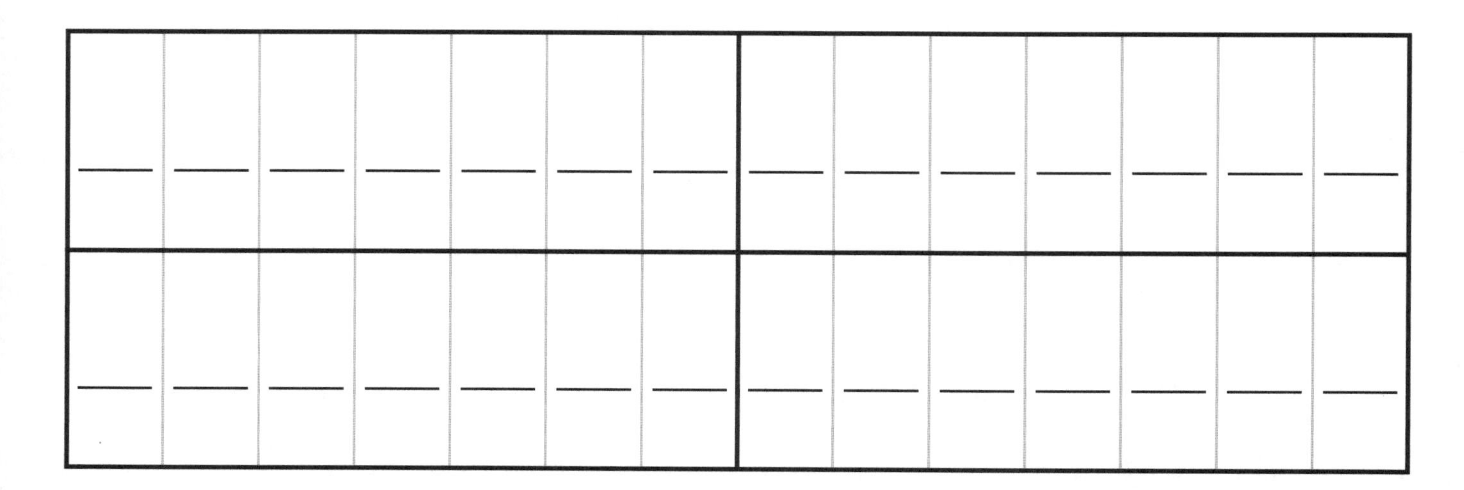

161

Answer these facts.

15	11	8	13	18	6
− 9	− 4	+ 9	− 5	− 9	+ 8

14	17	12	15	7	9	16	11
− 8	− 8	− 9	− 7	+ 8	+ 7	− 8	− 3

12	8	14	11	9	13	9	12
− 6	+ 6	− 7	− 6	+ 9	− 6	+ 5	− 4

8	12	8	15	15	12	9	13
+ 7	− 8	+ 8	− 6	− 8	− 7	+ 6	− 8

11	13	14	5	13	14	11	9
− 2	− 9	− 6	+ 9	− 4	− 9	− 7	+ 8

"His eye seeth every precious thing."
Job 28:10

6	12	13	7	11
+ 9	− 3	− 5	+ 9	− 5

Answer these problems. Carry or borrow in every problem.

38	56	29	98	48	76
+ 69	- 48	+ 77	- 59	+ 54	- 47
___	___	___	___	___	___

86	79	75	59	50	89
- 59	+ 79	- 49	+ 98	- 25	+ 67
___	___	___	___	___	___

95	79	78	37	57	65
- 87	+ 28	- 39	+ 69	- 28	+ 37
___	___	___	___	___	___

Answer these story problems.

Sister Miller's class went on a hike. Wayne threw peanuts to 3 squirrels scampering on the ground.

"Look!" whispered Dale. "There are 2 squirrels in the tree." Then 4 more squirrels appeared. How many squirrels were there then?

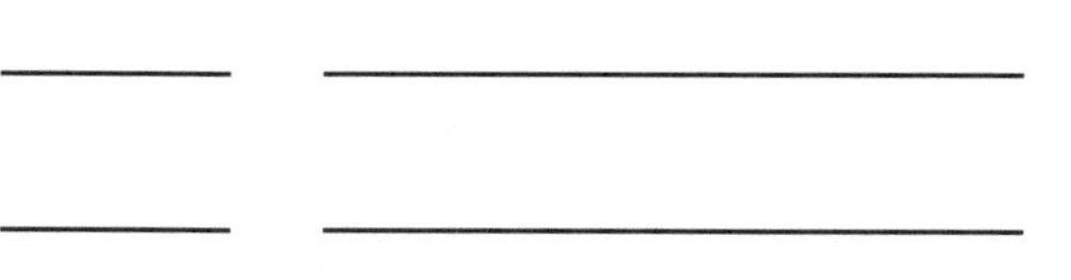

When Raymond rushed up too close, six squirrels scampered away. That left only _____ squirrels to finish eating the peanuts. (Use your total from the first problem.)

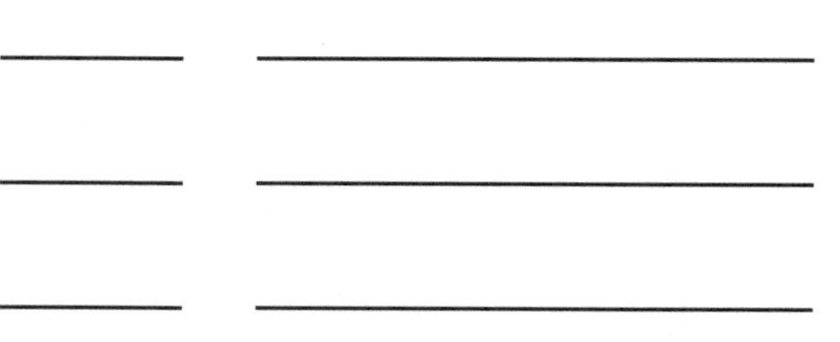

161 Write the time.

Write the missing time for each story.

1. The children in grade 2 sat down to eat lunch at 12:00. One hour later, at ______________ they were busily working again.
2. The buns need to bake for $\frac{1}{2}$ hour. Mother put them into the oven at 11:00. At ______________ they were finished baking.
3. Grandfather went outside at 4:00 for his regular 30-minute walk. He came back at ______________.
4. At 3:00 on Saturday, Mother said that Judy and Elaine were allowed to have 1 hour of playtime. They played until ______________.
5. Elmer worked for one hour, cleaning rabbit pens. He worked from 4:30 till ______________.

Work while you work, play while you play;
That is the way to be happy and gay.
Whatever you do, do with your might;
Things done by halves are never done right.

—Author unknown

Count the money. Add the amounts.

+

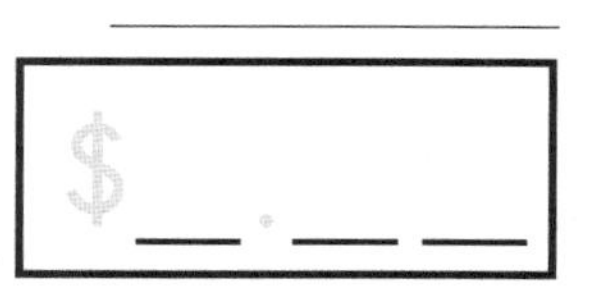

$ ___ . ___ ___

$

+ $

$ ___ . ___ ___

Count the money.

1. James put 3 **quarters** into the offering basket. ____________
2. Sharon put **6 dimes and 1 nickel** into her piggy bank. ____________
3. Father used **4 quarters and 3 dimes** to buy a stamp. ____________

"God loveth a cheerful giver" (2 Corinthians 9:7).

162

Answer these facts.

7	5	9	14	16	2	9	18
+ 7	+ 7	+ 7	− 6	− 7	+ 9	+ 6	− 9

7	17	8	6	9	5	18	8
+ 8	− 8	+ 4	+ 7	+ 9	+ 6	− 9	+ 6

8	9	15	4	8	9	5	7
+ 3	+ 8	− 7	+ 8	+ 8	+ 5	+ 8	+ 4

6	14	6	8	14	5	16	8
+ 9	− 8	+ 5	+ 9	− 5	+ 9	− 8	+ 5

7	15	7	4	4	17	6	8
+ 5	− 8	+ 9	+ 9	+ 7	− 9	+ 6	+ 7

"His eye seeth every precious thing."
Job 28:10

15	9	6	16	3
− 6	+ 2	+ 8	− 9	+ 8

Answer these problems. Carry when you need to.

$\begin{array}{r} 126 \\ -\ 95 \\ \hline \end{array}$	$\begin{array}{r} 78 \\ +\ 97 \\ \hline \end{array}$	$\begin{array}{r} 166 \\ -\ 94 \\ \hline \end{array}$	$\begin{array}{r} 158 \\ -\ 65 \\ \hline \end{array}$	$\begin{array}{r} 66 \\ +\ 96 \\ \hline \end{array}$	$\begin{array}{r} 168 \\ -\ 86 \\ \hline \end{array}$
$\begin{array}{r} 86 \\ -\ 83 \\ \hline \end{array}$	$\begin{array}{r} 179 \\ -\ 88 \\ \hline \end{array}$	$\begin{array}{r} 86 \\ +\ 97 \\ \hline \end{array}$	$\begin{array}{r} 127 \\ -\ 84 \\ \hline \end{array}$	$\begin{array}{r} 93 \\ +\ 75 \\ \hline \end{array}$	$\begin{array}{r} 189 \\ -\ 96 \\ \hline \end{array}$
$\begin{array}{r} 87 \\ +\ 88 \\ \hline \end{array}$	$\begin{array}{r} 119 \\ -\ 88 \\ \hline \end{array}$	$\begin{array}{r} 177 \\ -\ 84 \\ \hline \end{array}$	$\begin{array}{r} 159 \\ -\ 87 \\ \hline \end{array}$	$\begin{array}{r} 156 \\ -\ 74 \\ \hline \end{array}$	$\begin{array}{r} 87 \\ +\ 75 \\ \hline \end{array}$
$\begin{array}{r} 167 \\ -\ 76 \\ \hline \end{array}$	$\begin{array}{r} 95 \\ +\ 74 \\ \hline \end{array}$	$\begin{array}{r} 138 \\ -\ 95 \\ \hline \end{array}$	$\begin{array}{r} 85 \\ +\ 98 \\ \hline \end{array}$	$\begin{array}{r} 187 \\ -\ 94 \\ \hline \end{array}$	$\begin{array}{r} 69 \\ +\ 99 \\ \hline \end{array}$

Answer the story problem.

When Sister Miller's class went on a hike in Brother Martin's woods, the girls picked 23 spring flowers. But 15 of them wilted, so the girls threw them away. How many flowers were left to put in a vase?

162

Trace and finish the rules.

____ ________ = 1 yard

12 months = ____ ________

____ ________ = 1 pint

$\frac{2}{2}$ = ____ ________

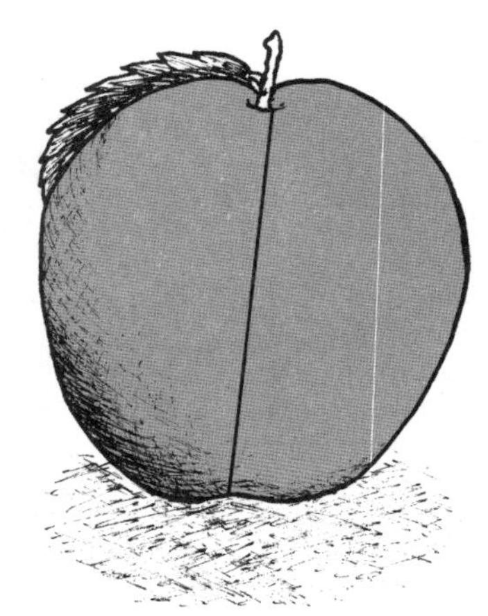

Answer these addition problems.

25	34	33	45	57	54
43	43	54	30	32	34
+99	+79	+78	+99	+96	+94
____	____	____	____	____	____

43	64	46	53	38	35
24	25	43	33	50	22
+15	+78	+67	+79	+86	+28
____	____	____	____	____	____

Speed Drill

9	17	9	16	9	7
+ 7	− 9	+ 9	− 9	+ 8	+ 9

He said,
"Peace, be still."
Mark 4:39

17	8	16	18	9	17
− 8	+ 9	− 7	− 9	+ 8	− 9

7	8	16	9	17	9	9	18
+ 9	+ 9	− 9	+ 9	− 8	+ 7	+ 8	− 9

6	3	5	4	7	8	4	5
2	6	4	4	2	1	3	3
+ 9	+ 7	+ 9	+ 9	+ 8	+ 9	+ 9	+ 9

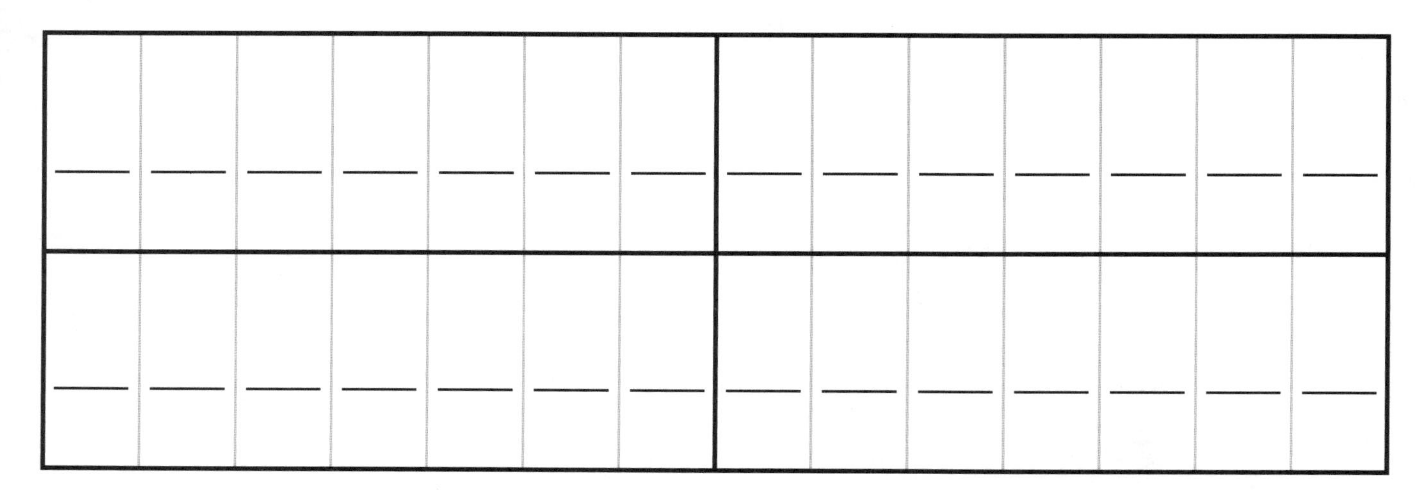

163 **Answer these facts.**

$16 - 7$	$6 + 9$	$11 - 4$	$17 - 9$	$12 - 3$	$8 + 9$	$5 + 6$	$11 - 9$
$15 - 6$	$6 + 6$	$8 + 8$	$12 - 8$	$9 + 2$	$11 - 5$	$8 + 7$	$9 + 3$
$17 - 8$	$8 + 3$	$9 + 8$	$12 - 4$	$4 + 7$	$15 - 8$	$11 - 8$	$9 + 7$
$6 + 5$	$12 - 6$	$8 + 4$	$9 + 8$	$11 - 3$	$3 + 9$	$16 - 8$	$12 - 7$
$15 - 9$	$7 + 5$	$7 + 9$	$11 - 7$	$18 - 9$	$4 + 8$	$11 - 2$	$9 + 9$

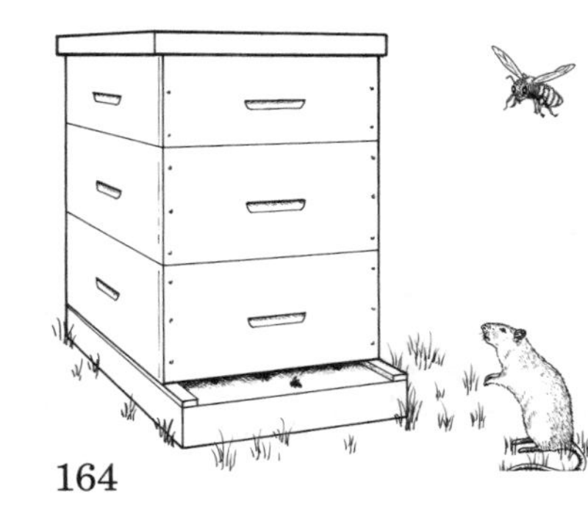

"His eye seeth every precious thing."
Job 28:10

$16 - 9$	$2 + 9$	$11 - 6$	$9 + 6$	$12 - 5$

Fill in the missing whole or part.

16 − ___ = 7	7 + ___ = 16	18 − ___ = 9
___ + 8 = 17	___ − 9 = 9	7 + 9 = ___
9 + 9 = ___	16 − ___ = 8	17 − ___ = 8
18 − ___ = 9	8 + 9 = ___	8 + ___ = 16
___ + 8 = 16	9 + ___ = 17	___ + 9 = 16
___ − 8 = 9	18 − 9 = ___	9 + ___ = 18

Answer these subtraction problems. You will not need to borrow.

1,698 − 926 = ___	1,872 − 941 = ___	1,698 − 834 = ___	1,763 − 810 = ___
1,184 − 563 = ___	1,359 − 837 = ___	1,166 − 743 = ___	1,276 − 952 = ___
1,474 − 702 = ___	1,689 − 736 = ___	1,585 − 721 = ___	1,858 − 927 = ___

163

Write a fraction for the shaded part of each picture.

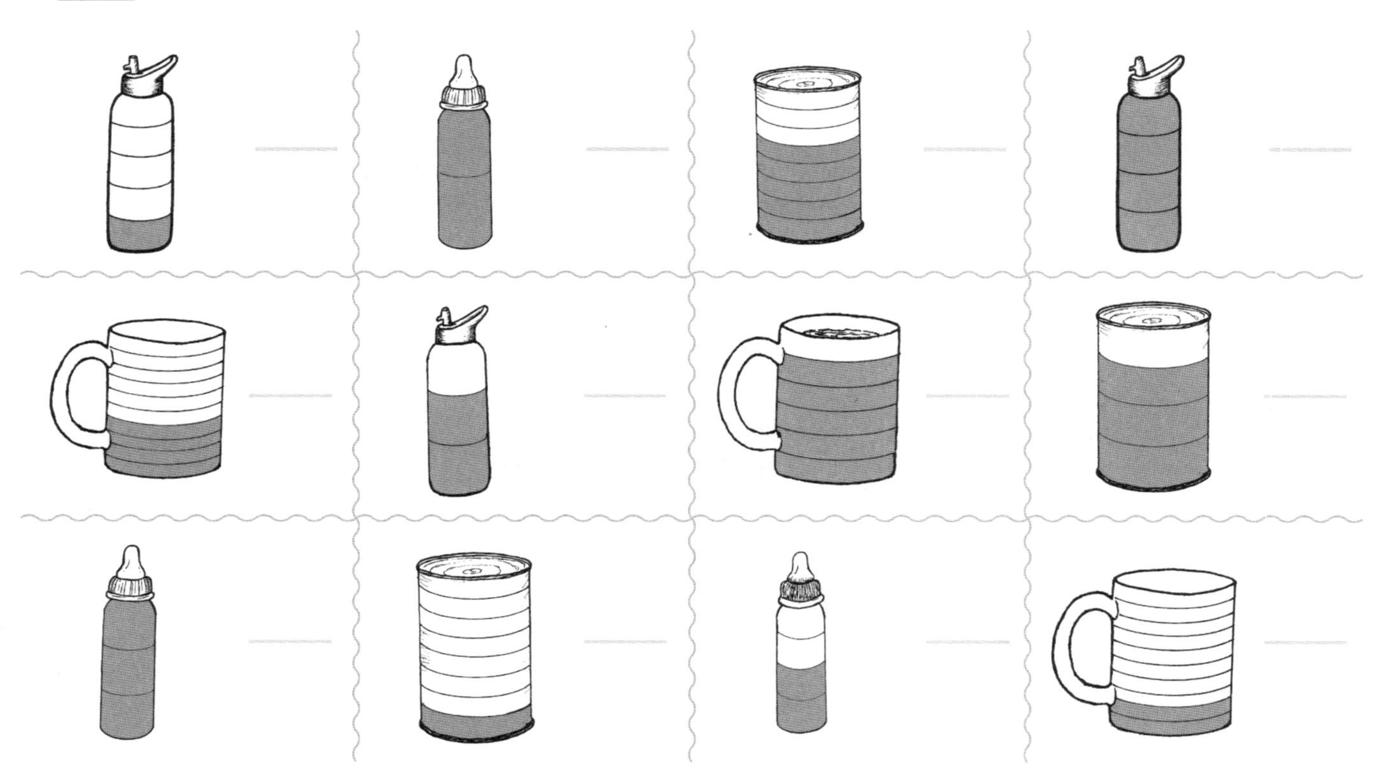

Answer these story problems.

Mother has one dozen buttons in a jar and 88 buttons in a box. How many buttons does Mother have altogether?

______ ________________

______ ________________

______ ________________

Fred and Fay played church. Fred preached for five minutes. They sang for nine minutes. How many minutes long was their church service?

______ ________________

______ ________________

______ ________________

Use the calendar page to answer the questions.

September						
Sunday	Monday	Tuesday	Wednesday	Thursday	Friday	Saturday
	1	2	3	4	5	6
7	8	9	10	11	12	13
14	15	16	17	18	19	20
21	22	23	24	25	26	27
28	29	30				

1. Name the days of the week.

_______________, _______________, _______________,

_______________, _______________,

_______________, _______________

2. September has __________ days.

3. Write the numbers (dates) that are Tuesdays.

________, ________, ________, ________, ________

4. John plans to go to his cousin's wedding on September 27. That will be on a _______________.

5. John's father is a minister. He went away to preach on September 12, 13, and 14. Which days of the week was he gone?

_______________, _______________, _______________

164 Answer these facts.

18 − 9	9 + 9	15 − 8	9 + 8	14 − 8	13 − 7	17 − 8	5 + 8
4 + 9	17 − 9	9 + 5	16 − 9	6 + 7	15 − 9	8 + 9	16 − 8
7 + 7	15 − 7	8 + 9	9 + 6	14 − 6	7 + 9	7 + 8	13 − 5
9 + 4	8 + 8	13 − 6	9 + 7	13 − 8	16 − 7	8 + 6	17 − 9
5 + 9	18 − 9	16 − 8	7 + 6	15 − 6	17 − 9	15 − 7	14 − 9

"His eye seeth every precious thing."
Job 28:10

8 + 7	14 − 5	16 − 7	8 + 5	13 − 4

Answer these problems. Carry when you need to.

78 + 69	179 − 96	65 + 85	179 − 84	37 + 26	159 − 81
168 − 73	82 + 82	79 + 26	178 − 94	69 + 99	139 − 98
158 − 75	89 + 58	157 − 62	56 + 94	168 − 90	29 + 34

91 + 73	187 − 92	167 − 83	88 + 17

Add commas to the numbers.
Circle the digit in the hundreds' place.

4561	3705	52890	304
75017	6132	78	20659

164

Trace and finish the rules.

16 ounces = ____ ________

____ ________ = 1 dozen

12 inches = ____ ________

Fill in the blanks.

1. Dorothy put 2 cups or ________ ____________ of sugar into the cookie dough.

2. Hannah put 1 dozen cookies into a bag.
   That was ________ cookies.

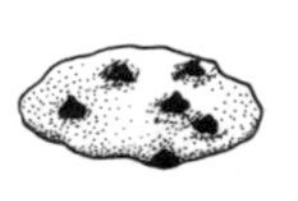

3. Anthony read for 5 minutes more than $\frac{1}{2}$ hour.
   For how many minutes did he read? ________ ____________
   (Think: $\frac{1}{2}$ hour = 30 minutes; plus 5 more minutes)

4. Little David is 1 year and 2 months old, or ________ months old.
   (Think: 1 year = 12 months; plus 2 more months)

5. Laura measured the cute little stove. It was 1 foot **less** than a yard wide.
   How many feet wide was it? ________ ____________
   (Think: 1 yard = 3 feet; take away 1 foot)

Speed Drill

"So run,
that ye may obtain."
1 Corinthians 9:24

17	9	4	18	12	7
− 8	+ 6	+ 9	− 9	− 9	+ 9

13	16	5	11	6	9
− 4	− 9	+ 9	− 9	+ 9	+ 9

14	9	3	15	9	17	14	9
− 5	+ 8	+ 9	− 6	+ 7	− 9	− 9	+ 4

13	9	16	9	9	15	12	8
− 9	+ 5	− 7	+ 9	+ 2	− 9	− 3	+ 9

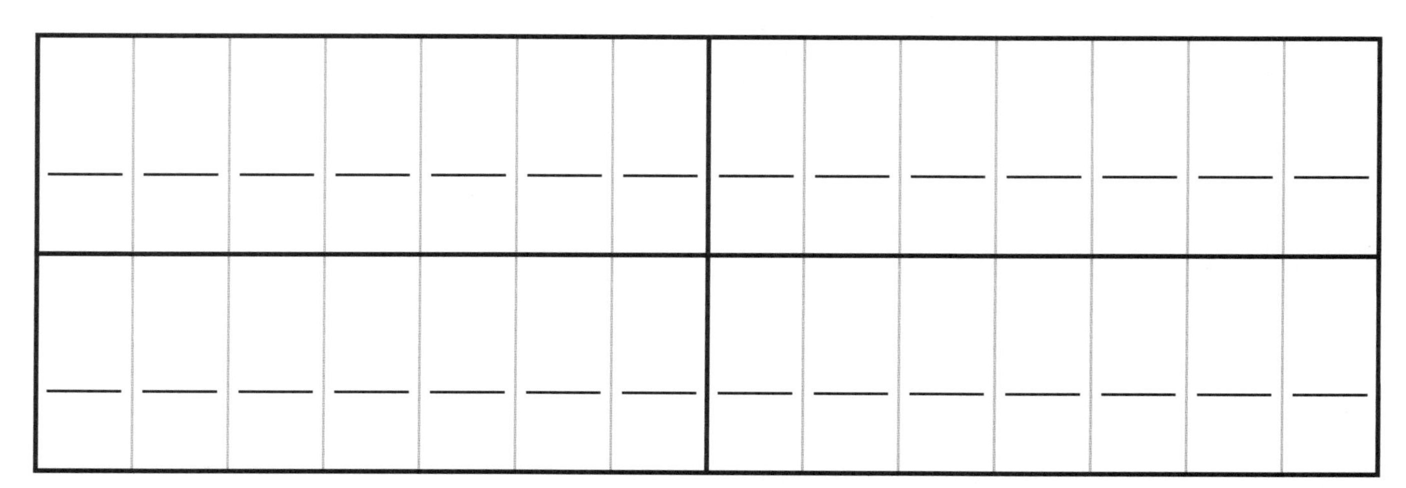

165 Answer these facts.

9	2	6	9	9	4	5	7
+ 6	+ 7	+ 8	+ 3	+ 9	+ 8	+ 4	+ 9

7	4	8	1	6	4	5	7
+ 3	+ 7	+ 9	+ 9	+ 7	+ 6	+ 9	+ 5

3	6	8	5	3	6	9	5
+ 9	+ 3	+ 8	+ 8	+ 6	+ 5	+ 8	+ 5

4	3	6	5	8	9	4	6
+ 5	+ 8	+ 9	+ 7	+ 2	+ 7	+ 9	+ 4

2	8	6	8	7	9	1
+ 8	+ 9	+ 6	+ 6	+ 4	+ 9	+ 8

"His eye seeth every precious thing."
Job 28:10

3	7	9	2	9
+ 7	+ 8	+ 5	+ 9	+ 8

Answer these subtraction problems. Borrow once in each problem.

769	877	694	966	788
-586	-158	-138	-357	-393

755	991	939	888	981
-328	-808	-544	-279	-425

950	984	677
-231	-557	-494

Answer these questions.

Lena chose 6 apples for the lunches. Half of them were red; how many were red? _____ ____________

18 calves pranced across the fresh green grass. One-half of them were black. How many were not black? _____ ____________

Fourteen balloons waited for playtime. When playtime was over, half of them had popped. How many balloons were still good? _____ ____________

Ten bluebird houses stood on the pasture fence posts. One-half of them got used. How many houses were empty? _____ ____________

165

Measure these pencils.

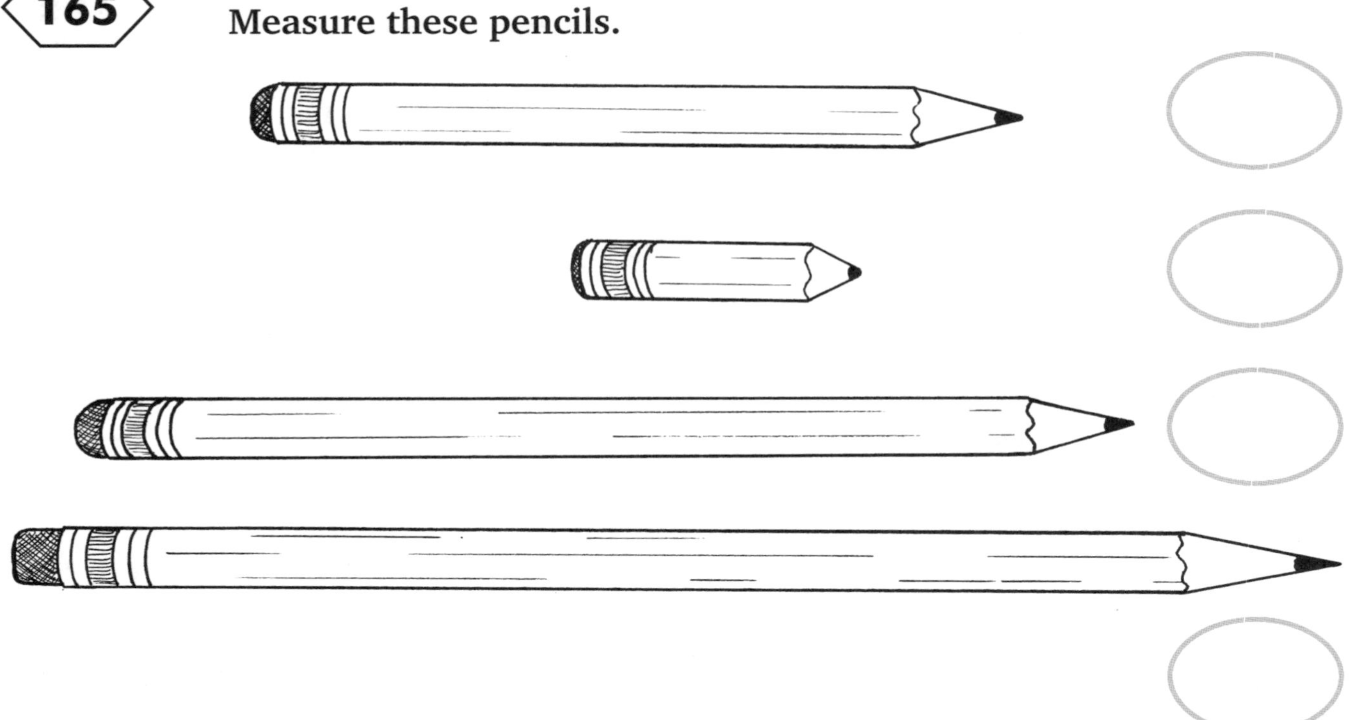

Answer these story problems.

Uzziah was a good king of Judah. He was 16 years old when he was made king, and he reigned for 52 years. How many years old was Uzziah when he died?

Jesus called 12 disciples to help Him in His work while He lived on earth. When 3 disciples went up a mountain with Him, how many were not with Him?

Jacob prepared 580 animals to give to Esau. The goats and sheep numbered 440. How many animals were not sheep and goats?

Study the line graph, and answer the questions.

165

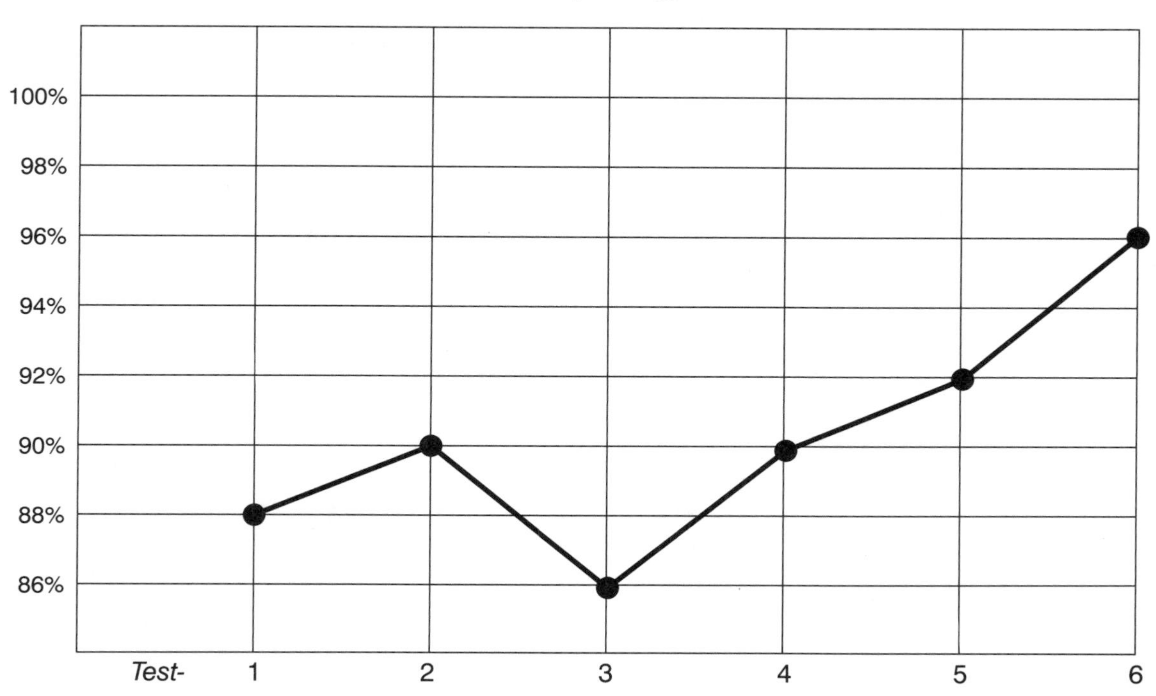

1. On which test did Carl have the lowest score? ____________

   What was the score? ____________

2. Which score did Carl have two times? ____________

   On which tests was that score? ____________, ____________

3. How many times was Carl's score lower than 90%? ____________

4. How many times was Carl's score higher than 90%? ____________

5. *Why do you think* Carl's score kept climbing for the last three tests?

   ____

166 Answer these facts.

14 - 5	12 - 3	17 - 8	13 - 7	9 - 1	15 - 7	11 - 4	16 - 7
12 - 6	16 - 9	9 - 3	13 - 4	11 - 3	18 - 9	10 - 4	14 - 6
11 - 9	13 - 8	9 - 5	15 - 6	12 - 5	11 - 8	14 - 9	10 - 6
9 - 2	18 - 9	10 - 3	11 - 5	14 - 7	9 - 6	13 - 5	16 - 8
12 - 7	10 - 2	15 - 8	12 - 4	17 - 8	13 - 9	9 - 4	14 - 8

"His eye seeth every precious thing."
Job 28:10

13 - 6	10 - 1	16 - 7	12 - 8	15 - 9

Answer these problems. Carry one or two times in each problem.

749 +549	559 +808	577 +579	577 +788
558 +699	969 +507	867 +389	728 +738
787 +369	928 +439	859 +439	

Answer these story problems.

The Bible tells about a man that had six fingers on each hand. How many fingers did he have on both hands?

The same man had six toes on each foot. How many toes was that?

How many fingers and toes did this man have altogether?

fingers
toes
fingers and toes

How many fingers and toes do *you* have altogether?

166

Write a fraction for the shaded part of each shape.
Circle the shapes that show fractions the same as $\frac{1}{2}$.

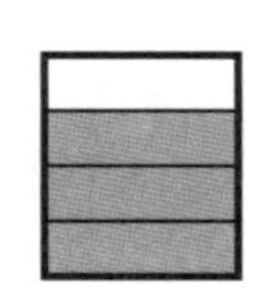 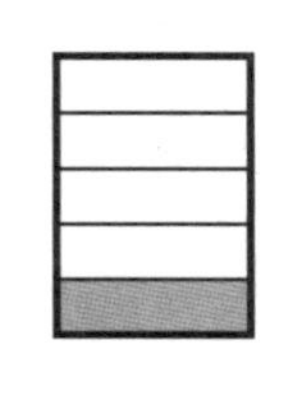 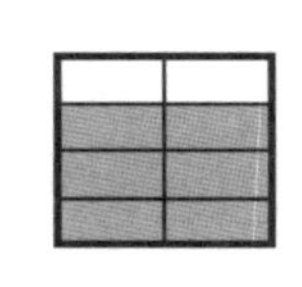 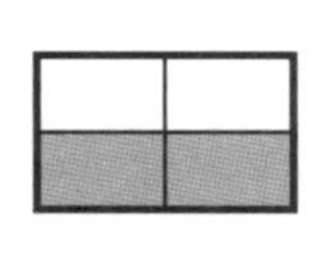 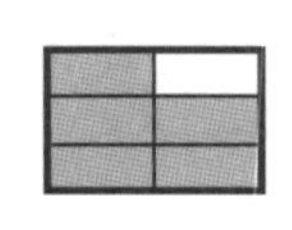

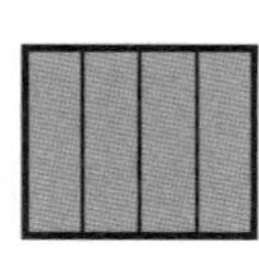 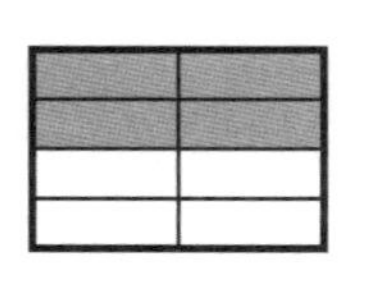 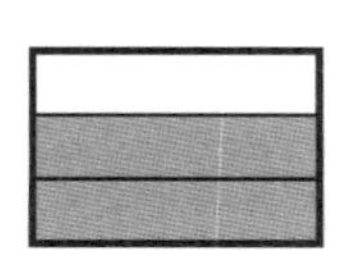 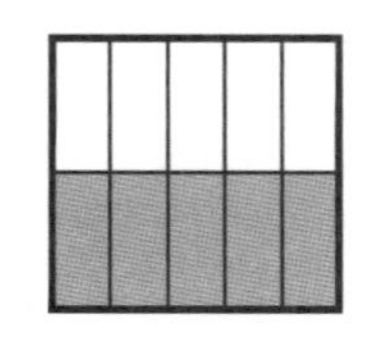 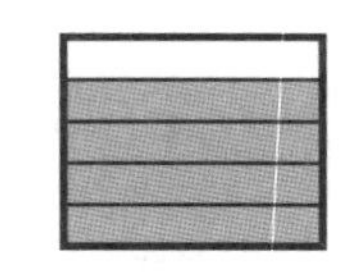

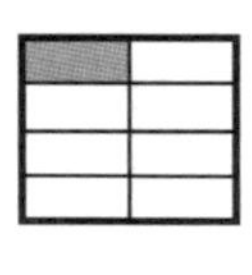 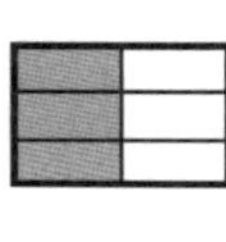 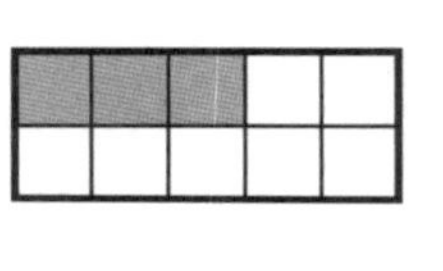 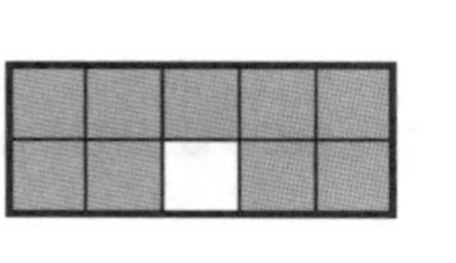 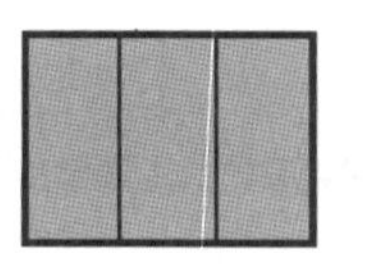

Round these numbers to the nearest ten.

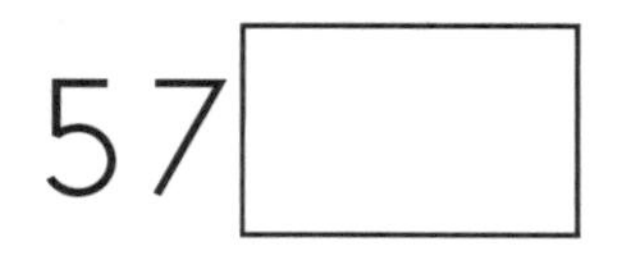

57 ☐ 65 ☐ 92 ☐ 28 ☐

13 ☐ 41 ☐ 76 ☐ 84 ☐

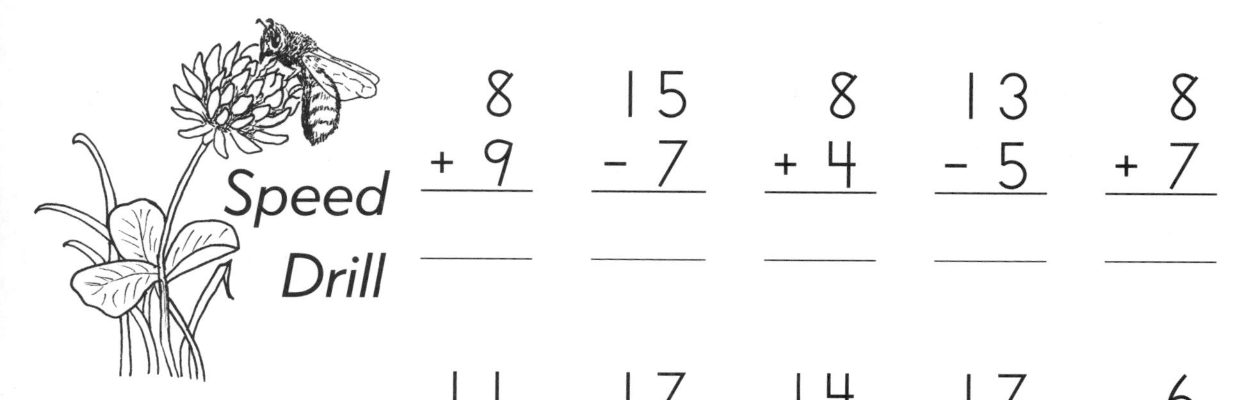

Speed Drill

"Whatsoever thy hand findeth to do, do it with thy might."
Ecclesiastes 9:10

8	15	8	13	8	16
+ 9	− 7	+ 4	− 5	+ 7	− 8

11	17	14	17	6	8
− 8	− 8	− 8	− 9	+ 8	+ 3

4	13	9	8	12	15	5	7
+ 8	− 8	+ 8	+ 6	− 8	− 8	+ 8	+ 8

17	11	8	14	3	8	12	8
− 8	− 3	+ 9	− 6	+ 8	+ 8	− 4	+ 5

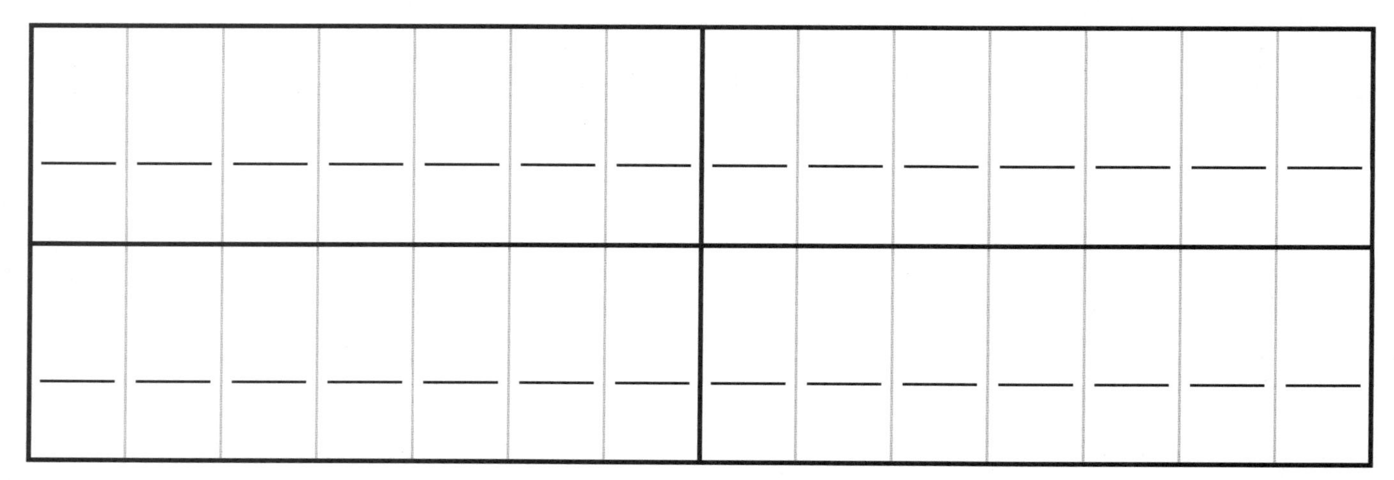

167 Answer these facts.

"His eye seeth every precious thing."
Job 28:10

14 − 6	16 − 7	9 + 5	8 + 7	16 − 8

17 − 8	8 + 7	14 − 7	8 + 8	8 + 6	14 − 5	5 + 9	15 − 8
14 − 8	16 − 9	14 − 10	18 − 9	9 + 8	8 + 8	15 − 8	7 + 9
9 + 9	6 + 8	14 − 7	8 + 9	17 − 8	16 − 8	7 + 7	15 − 9
17 − 9	14 − 8	9 + 6	17 − 8	7 + 8	17 − 9	6 + 9	8 + 6
6 + 8	15 − 7	18 − 9	14 − 5	9 + 7	14 − 6	9 + 9	15 − 7

Do these number strings.

5 + 4 + 4 − 6 + 5 = ___

18 − 9 − 2 + 3 + 5 = ___

16 − 8 + 7 − 6 + 8 = ___

3 + 4 + 4 − 2 + 9 = ___

7 + 9 − 8 − 5 + 7 = ___

5 + 9 − 7 + 9 − 8 = ___

Use the calendar page to answer the questions.

October						
Sunday	Monday	Tuesday	Wednesday	Thursday	Friday	Saturday
			1	2	3	4
5	6	7	8	9	10	11
12	13	14	15	16	17	18
19	20	21	22	23	24	25
26	27	28	29	30	31	

1. This is the month of ____________________.

2. The Millers traveled to Wisconsin on October 18. Which day of the week was that? ____________________

3. The Millers returned home on October 23. Which day of the week was that? ____________________

4. The Zooks had dinner guests on the second Sunday of the month. That was on October ________.

167 **Answer these problems. Carry or borrow in every problem.**

$$\begin{array}{r} 94 \\ -\ 55 \\ \hline \end{array} \quad \begin{array}{r} 38 \\ +\ 46 \\ \hline \end{array} \quad \begin{array}{r} 74 \\ -\ 37 \\ \hline \end{array} \quad \begin{array}{r} 57 \\ -\ 28 \\ \hline \end{array} \quad \begin{array}{r} 47 \\ +\ 57 \\ \hline \end{array} \quad \begin{array}{r} 94 \\ -\ 28 \\ \hline \end{array}$$

$$\begin{array}{r} 28 \\ +\ 59 \\ \hline \end{array} \quad \begin{array}{r} 58 \\ -\ 19 \\ \hline \end{array} \quad \begin{array}{r} 96 \\ -\ 67 \\ \hline \end{array} \quad \begin{array}{r} 85 \\ -\ 48 \\ \hline \end{array} \quad \begin{array}{r} 85 \\ -\ 19 \\ \hline \end{array} \quad \begin{array}{r} 75 \\ +\ 29 \\ \hline \end{array}$$

$$\begin{array}{r} 39 \\ +\ 68 \\ \hline \end{array} \quad \begin{array}{r} 86 \\ -\ 38 \\ \hline \end{array} \quad \begin{array}{r} 97 \\ -\ 39 \\ \hline \end{array} \quad \begin{array}{r} 94 \\ -\ 46 \\ \hline \end{array} \quad \begin{array}{r} 85 \\ -\ 27 \\ \hline \end{array} \quad \begin{array}{r} 27 \\ +\ 78 \\ \hline \end{array}$$

Answer these story problems.

Grandfather had 37 kids in his flock of goats. He sold eight kids. How many kids did he have then?

_____ _______________

_____ _______________

_____ _______________

After a rainy week, the grass was extra tall. Father cut the grass, and the boys raked it into 16 heaps. They dumped 7 heaps on the garden. How many heaps were left?

_____ _______________

_____ _______________

_____ _______________

Count the money. Add the amounts.

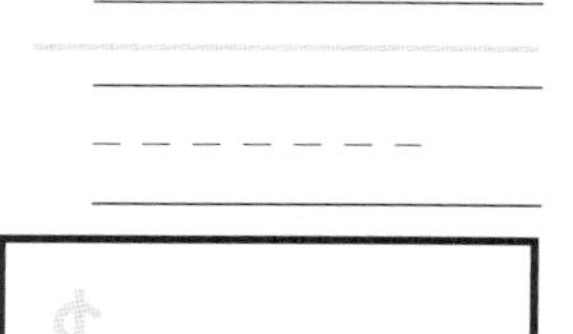

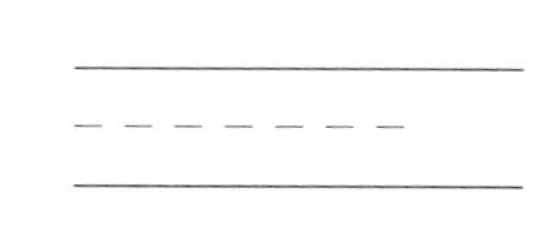

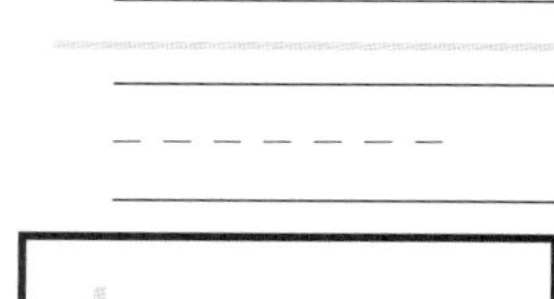

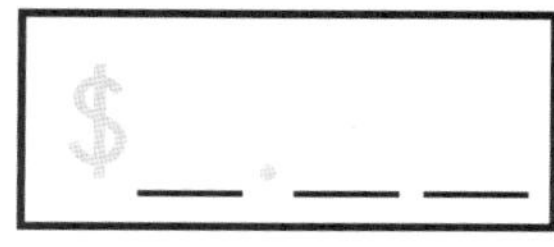

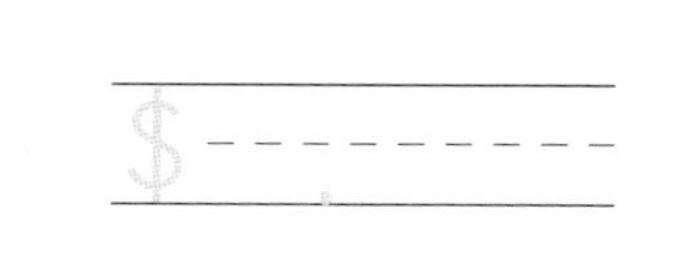

168 Answer these facts.

$8 + 4$	$9 + 8$	$4 + 6$	$6 + 2$	$9 + 6$	$8 + 6$	$5 + 4$	$9 + 7$
$2 + 8$	$7 + 8$	$5 + 9$	$1 + 6$	$3 + 8$	$3 + 5$	$8 + 5$	$4 + 8$
$7 + 9$	$3 + 6$	$8 + 9$	$7 + 5$	$9 + 9$	$2 + 5$	$4 + 9$	$7 + 3$
$4 + 7$	$9 + 3$	$2 + 6$	$8 + 7$	$5 + 2$	$1 + 9$	$5 + 6$	$8 + 8$
$3 + 7$	$9 + 9$	$5 + 8$	$7 + 2$	$2 + 9$	$7 + 7$	$3 + 4$	$6 + 9$

"His eye seeth every precious thing."
Job 28:10

$7 + 9$	$6 + 7$	$5 + 5$	$1 + 7$	$8 + 9$

Answer these problems. Carry when you need to.

168

169 − 87	68 + 27	179 − 94	157 − 85	73 + 86	166 − 76
72 + 74	159 − 62	93 + 85	156 − 94	86 + 37	177 − 84
144 − 54	84 + 75	168 − 96	147 − 62	66 + 29	156 − 74
188 − 95	64 + 59	148 − 86	84 + 94	137 − 40	53 + 93

Add commas to the numbers.
Circle the digit in the thousands' place.

491 6825 24537 9605

68254 92470 618 12769

168 **Answer these addition problems.**

55	64	52	13	63	52
24	24	36	66	24	27
+78	+46	+92	+97	+56	+83
____	____	____	____	____	____

52	41	35	10	46	64
36	27	52	59	33	24
+69	+75	+89	+39	+55	+74
____	____	____	____	____	____

Fill in the blanks.

1. Sandra ate 2 halves of an apple. She ate ________ ____________ apple.

2. The young tree was 1 yard tall, or ________ feet tall.

3. A juice bottle holds 1 pint and 1 cup, or ________ cups of juice. (Think: 1 pint = 2 cups; plus 1 more cup)

4. A sheet of red paper was 1 inch **less** than 1 foot. The paper was ________ inches long. (Think: 1 foot = 12 inches; take away 1 inch)

Speed Drill

"Learn
to do well."
Isaiah 1:1

15	12	16	14	11	12
- 6	- 6	- 8	- 7	- 4	- 3

11	12	15	13	18	14
- 2	- 5	- 7	- 6	- 9	- 6

13	17	11	14	12	11	13	16
- 4	- 8	- 5	- 5	- 4	- 3	- 5	- 7

4	3	7	4	2	6	1	6
3	5	2	2	5	3	7	2
+5	+7	+8	+5	+7	+9	+8	+5

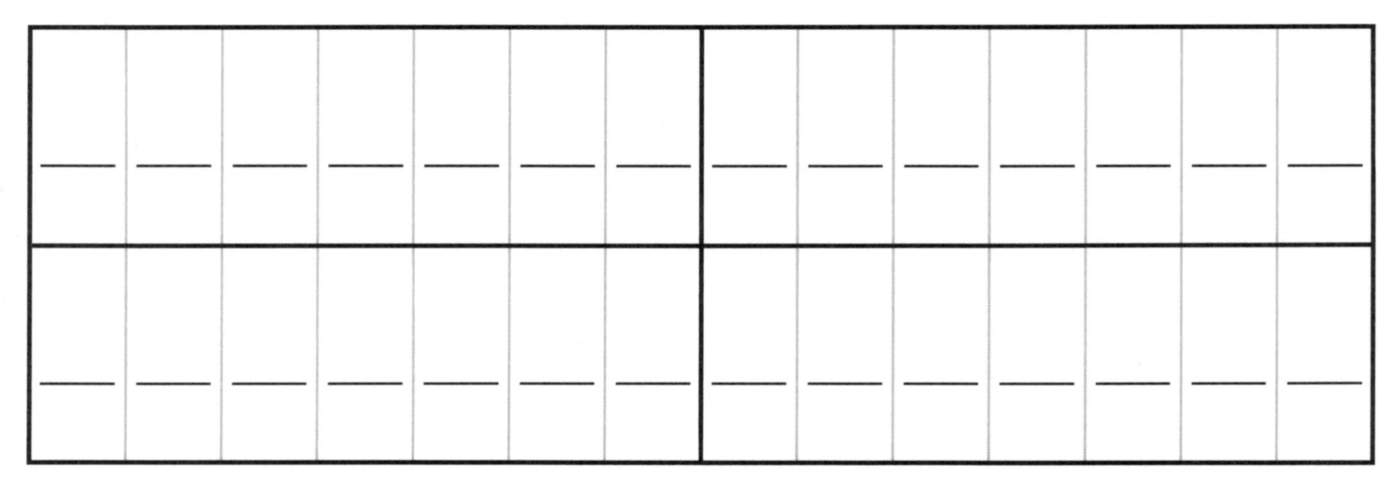

169 Answer these facts.

16	8	14	11	17
− 7	− 5	− 7	− 3	− 8

9	12	18	14	12	7	15	10
− 8	− 8	− 9	− 8	− 3	− 3	− 6	− 8

15	11	13	10	17	11	9	14
− 8	− 7	− 4	− 5	− 9	− 2	− 5	− 5

10	7	16	13	10	15	8	18
− 6	− 5	− 9	− 6	− 9	− 7	− 7	− 9

9	17	11	10	14	9	12	16
− 9	− 8	− 4	− 4	− 6	− 7	− 4	− 8

10	8	13	12	18	11	16	9
− 7	− 6	− 5	− 6	− 9	− 5	− 7	− 6

Fill in the missing whole or part.

9 + 7 = ___	17 − ___ = 9	9 + ___ = 15
___ + 9 = 17	___ − 4 = 9	___ + 8 = 17
18 − ___ = 9	7 + ___ = 16	11 − ___ = 9
9 + ___ = 14	12 − 9 = ___	9 + 9 = ___
16 − 7 = ___	___ − 9 = 8	6 + ___ = 15
___ − 9 = 6	5 + ___ = 14	___ − 7 = 9

Answer these problems. Borrow once in each problem.

969 −390 ___	781 −403 ___	880 −434 ___	997 −729 ___	918 −373 ___
829 −561 ___	638 −192 ___	993 −615 ___	788 −209 ___	
610 −430 ___	785 −677 ___	944 −273 ___	890 −273 ___	

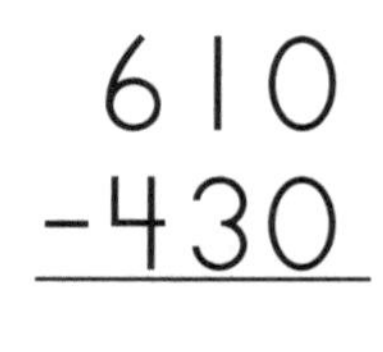

169

Write the name for each shape: circle, square, rectangle, triangle.

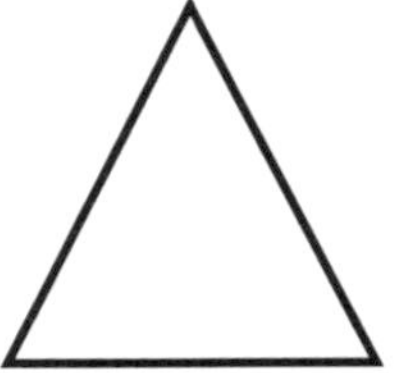

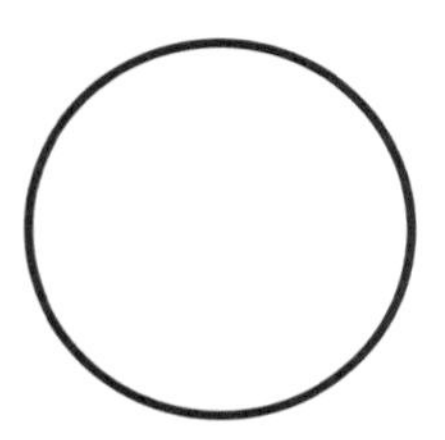

___________ ___________ ___________

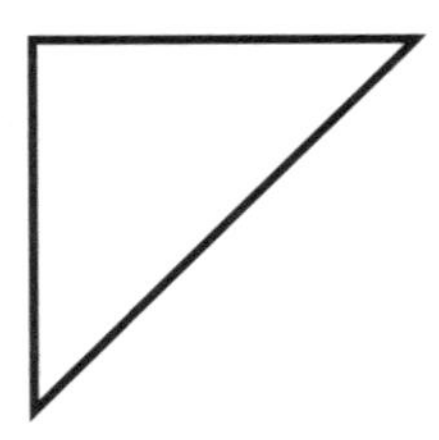

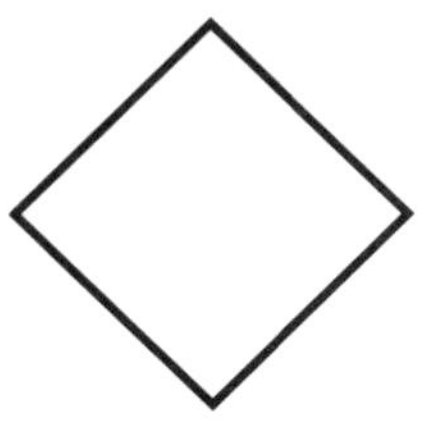

___________ ___________ ___________

Answer these story problems.

Rachel paid 89¢ for a yellow pansy and 89¢ for a purple pansy. What was the total for both flowers?

____

____

____

Mother planted 36 petunias and 27 marigolds. How many more petunias than marigolds did Mother plant?

___ ___________

___ ___________

___ ___________

Draw hands to make the clock show 3:30

Use the clock to answer the questions.

1. What time will it be

   – in 1 hour? ____________________

   – in 3 hours? ____________________

   – in $\frac{1}{2}$ hour? ____________________

2. What time was it

   – $\frac{1}{2}$ hour ago? ____________________

   – one hour ago? ____________________

   – 2 hours ago? ____________________

❖ Extra: Can you do these? ❖

What time was it 10 minutes ago?

____

What time was it 20 minutes ago?

____

170 Answer these facts.

11 − 6	15 − 9	9 + 9	7 + 5			16 − 9	11 − 9
16 − 8	17 − 8	4 + 7	12 − 8	7 + 8	17 − 9	8 + 6	13 − 8
6 + 6	9 + 9	14 − 9	16 − 7	2 + 9	9 + 8	12 − 9	8 + 8
6 + 9	9 + 7	11 − 8	15 − 7	4 + 9	12 − 7	8 − 7	13 − 7
17 − 8	7 + 7			8 + 4	14 − 8	8 + 9	8 + 3
13 − 9	9 + 6	3 + 9	18 − 9	11 − 7	9 + 5	15 − 6	7 + 9

Answer these problems. Carry or borrow in every problem.

35	95	27	86	49	76
+ 69	− 58	+ 78	− 48	+ 57	− 37
98	76	66	48	69	98
− 79	+ 94	− 59	+ 56	+ 38	− 39
87	78	36	94	82	74
− 28	+ 29	+ 68	− 87	+ 88	− 55

Answer these story problems.

78 bees buzz out of a hive. 67 bees follow them. How many bees is that altogether?

Eighteen drops of honey drip onto Joy's bun. She eats 9 drops. How many drops are left on her bun?

"How sweet are thy words unto my taste! Yea, sweeter than honey to my mouth."
Psalm 119:103

170

Answer these problems. Carry once or twice in each problem.

933	774	763	716	643
+928	+746	+255	+987	+999

776	864	726	670	944
+866	+839	+592	+850	+917

Study the bar graph and answer the questions.

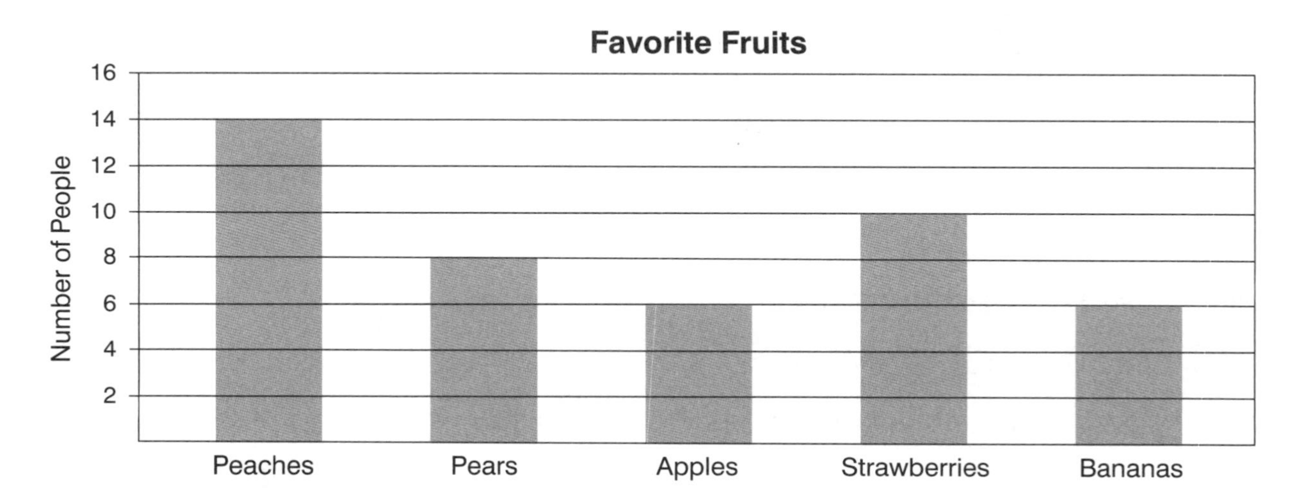

1. Which fruit was liked the best? __________

2. Which two kinds were liked the same?

   __________ __________

3. How many people liked strawberries? __________

4. How many more people liked peaches than pears? __________

5. How many liked strawberries and bananas? __________

6. Which do *you* like best? __________

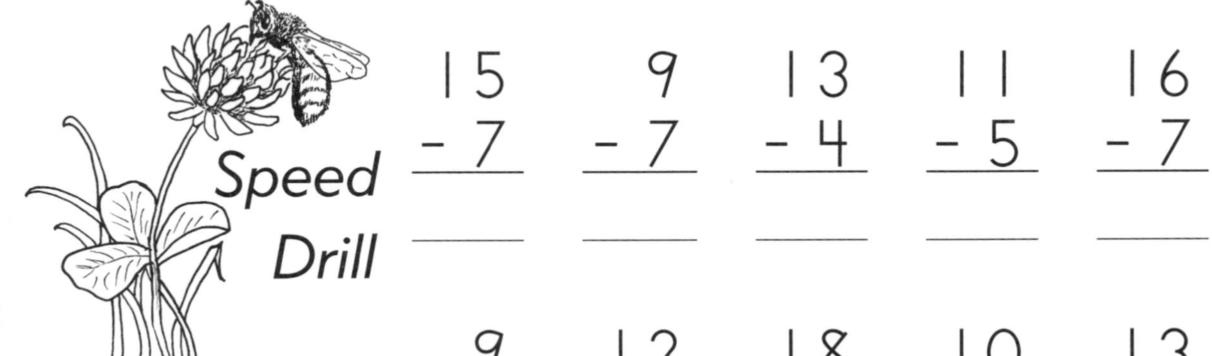

Speed Drill

"His eye seeth every precious thing."
Job 28:10

$15 - 7$	$9 - 7$	$13 - 4$	$11 - 5$	$16 - 7$	$10 - 4$
$9 - 5$	$12 - 5$	$18 - 9$	$10 - 7$	$13 - 6$	$14 - 5$

$12 - 4$	$17 - 8$	$9 - 6$	$14 - 6$	$13 - 5$	$10 - 8$	$15 - 6$	$11 - 3$
$2 + 4 + 4$	$3 + 6 + 8$	$1 + 5 + 6$	$4 + 3 + 4$	$2 + 5 + 7$	$6 + 2 + 2$	$5 + 4 + 7$	$2 + 7 + 9$

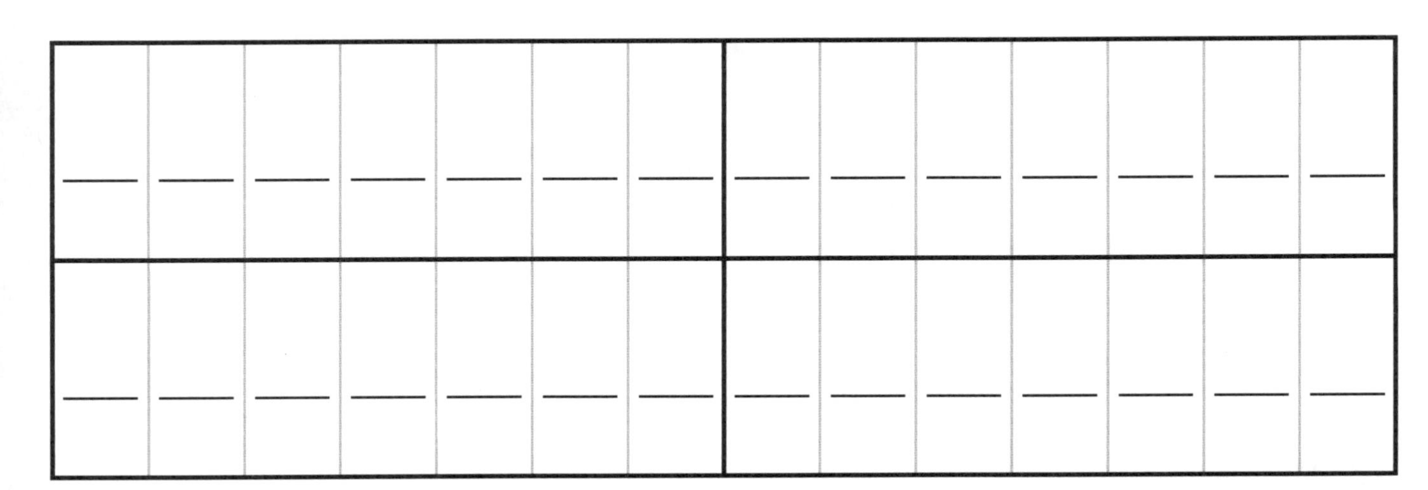